The Open University

Science: a second level course

ST240

OUR CHEMICAL ENVIRONMENT

BOOK 1 MODELS OF MATTER

Prepared for the Course Team by
David Roberts and (in part) Alan Bassindale

The Open University

ST240 Course Team

Course Team Chair	Stuart Bennett
General editors	Michael Mortimer
	Malcolm Rose
Authors	Rod Barratt
	Alan Bassindale
	Stuart Bennett
	Michael Gagan
	Jim Iley
	Michael Mortimer
	David Roberts
	Malcolm Rose
	Peter Taylor
Course Manager	Charlotte Sweeney
Course Secretary	Sally Eaton
BBC	Cameron Balbirnie
	Sandra Budin
	Andrew Law
	Paul Manners
	Michael Peet
	Nicholas Watson
	Darren Wycherley
Editors	Gerry Bearman
	Dick Sharp
Graphic Design	Sue Dobson
	Mark Kesby
	Mike Levers
	David Roberts
	Howard Taylor
	Rob Williams
Experimental work	Keith Cavanagh
	Ray Jones
	Pravin Patel

The Open University, Walton Hall, Milton Keynes, MK7 6AA

First published 1995; reprinted 2000

Edited, designed and typeset by The Open University.

Printed in the United Kingdom by Bath Press Ltd, Glasgow.

ISBN 0 7492 51417

This text forms part of an Open University Second Level Course. If you would like a copy of Studying with The Open University, please write to the Central Enquiry Service, PO Box 200, The Open University, Walton Hall, Milton Keynes, MK7 6YZ. If you have not enrolled on the Course and would like to buy this or other Open University material, please write to Open University Educational Enterprises Ltd, 12 Cofferidge Close, Stony Stratford, Milton Keynes, MK11 1BY, United Kingdom.

1.2

ST240book1i1.2

Contents

Chapter 1
Our global environment

Figure 1.1
Spaceship Earth. This view shows Africa near the top, slightly left of centre, with the Arabian Gulf and the Sahara Desert clearly visible. Near the bottom is Antarctica, brilliant in the Austral Summer.

The Earth. Seen from space. A picture we have seen many times. It was taken from a distance of 35 000 kilometres on 7 December 1972 by *Apollo 17* astronaut Harrison Schmitt, en route to the Moon during the last of the six successful lunar missions. Yet we should not underestimate the impact of this image. One effect, according to astronomer Fred Hoyle, was the almost universal awareness of the fragile nature of the global environment that emerged around that time. In 1948, long before manned space flight was possible, Hoyle had observed:

> *Once a photograph of the Earth, taken from outside, is available, we shall, in an emotional sense, acquire an additional dimension … Once let the sheer isolation of the Earth become plain … and a new idea as powerful as any in history will be let loose.*
>
> *(J. Darius,* Beyond Vision, *Oxford University Press, 1984, p. 142)*

Two decades after his original observation, Hoyle returned to it in a speech in Houston, one of the main control centres for the space programme:

> *Well, we now have such a photograph, and I've been wondering how this old prediction stands up. Has any new idea in fact been let loose? It certainly has. You will have noticed how quite suddenly everybody has become seriously concerned to protect the natural environment. Where has this idea come from? You could say from biologists, conservationists and ecologists. But they have been saying the same things as they're saying now for many years. Previously they never got on base. Something new has happened to create a world-wide awareness of our planet as a unique and precious place. It seems to me more than a coincidence that this awareness should have happened at exactly the moment man [sic] took his first step into space.*
>
> (*J. Darius,* Beyond Vision, *Oxford University Press, 1984, p. 142*)

Arguments still rage about whether the estimated cost of landing men on the Moon, some 24 billion dollars, was money well spent. However, there is little doubt that the space programme in general has, in a variety of ways, led to numerous developments that the majority would view as desirable. One of the most profound has been the ability to place satellites in orbit around the Earth (Figure 1.2). Despite the huge expense involved in the launching of satellites, a report to the Third Space Flight Conference in 1968 estimated that the eventual total value of the resulting benefits will exceed the total cost by a ratio of 20 to 1.

Perhaps the best-known consequence of satellite technology has been the effect on communications. Not only is it now possible to dial directly and speak with someone across the other side of the globe as clearly as if they lived in the same street, but television images of clarity equal to locally transmitted signals are routine. Indeed, many TV channels are available only by satellite. Reporters are heard in remote areas of the world by means of individual telephones that are able to transmit via a satellite. Ships and aircraft now rely on satellites for navigation and for relaying their position when in distress (Figure 1.3).

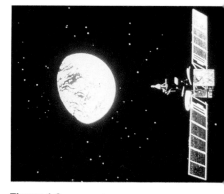

Figure 1.2
An Intelsat V communications satellite in geostationary orbit about the Earth. These satellites can handle up to 15 000 telephone circuits and two television channels.

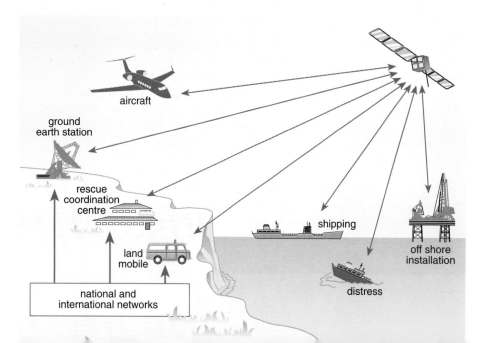

Figure 1.3
Satellite communications.

Figure 1.4
Typhoon Odessa, about 1 200 miles north of Hawaii, pictured during the voyage of the space shuttle *Discovery*, from 27 August to 3 September, 1985.

Figure 1.5
The mouth of the Mississippi River in the Gulf of Mexico, showing the formation of channels from soil transported from the Mississippi–Missouri–Ohio basin.

Satellites have many other uses, the majority of which are environmental in application. They provide invaluable data for weather forecasting: cloud formation can be observed throughout the atmosphere, and hurricanes and other storms can be observed and their movements tracked, for example (Figure 1.4). The mapping of the entire surface of the Earth and the location of mineral resources; information on vegetation, both wild and cultivated, for use in forestry and agriculture; the direct observation of natural processes that change the landscape (Figure 1.5); and monitoring the composition of the atmosphere: these are all examples that we now take for granted, yet have become possible only within the past couple of decades. They have been made possible by the programmes of satellite launches mounted mainly by the USA, the former USSR, Japan, and a consortium of European States.

Data obtained from satellites have played an important role in heightening our awareness that human activities have affected the environment on a major scale, notably the destruction of stratospheric ozone by chlorofluorocarbons (CFCs) and the potential effect on the climate of increasing levels of carbon dioxide in the Earth's atmosphere. Other more earthbound examples of environmental change are the widespread contamination of the environment by lead from leaded petrol and the pollution of lakes, rivers and groundwater in general by acid rain and fertilizers such as nitrates. All these are the by-products of the rapid growth of industrialization during the 20th century. They are all the result of scientific or technical developments of one kind or another, and many are chemically based. As a consequence, to a large section of the population, chemistry and things chemical are viewed as being undesirable because of the blame attached for such pollution (Figure 1.6).

"And as for Research and Development, Stevens–you people haven't come up with a new toxic substance in three months."

Figure 1.6
A not uncommon view of the chemical industry!

Such a public image is undoubtedly deserved in some cases, although the many benefits that chemistry has brought about are often overlooked. Further, it should perhaps be pointed out that it is, in part, the increasing sophistication and sensitivity of modern scientific instrumentation that has enabled certain types of pollution to be detected and monitored. Furthermore, removing the pollution and developing other solutions to the original problems will depend on continued research, albeit within a climate that favours a more environmentally sensitive approach than perhaps was common in the past. The finite and fragile nature of our global environment is now clearly realized by the vast majority of scientists.

Those of us involved in writing this Course believe that it is not possible to understand our environment, and our relationship to it, without involving chemistry, hence the Course title *Our Chemical Environment*. Chemistry is a subject unique in its breadth and scope. Because of this breadth and diversity it is not easy to say in a few words what chemistry, or this Course, is about. If you just look at some of the titles of different parts of the Course you will find subjects as apparently diverse as materials, energy, food, health, and perfumes (Figure 1.7).

Certainly, one of the aims of this Course is to provide you with the knowledge and skills to be able to understand and assess the impact of chemically based developments, and to evaluate for yourself the likely balance between beneficial and detrimental effects. There is no denying that pollution, poverty, malnutrition and disease are massive global problems. How can chemistry help to solve them? How is it already helping? Does its study help us to understand the trade-off between prosperity and pollution? What are the inevitable costs of living in a highly developed and industrialized society? You will already have your own views on these questions and so do we, but there are no simple answers.

When you have studied the Course, we hope that you will feel better able to understand the problems and feel that your views are more informed. But that is not the only aim. What we are also interested in is the excitement of

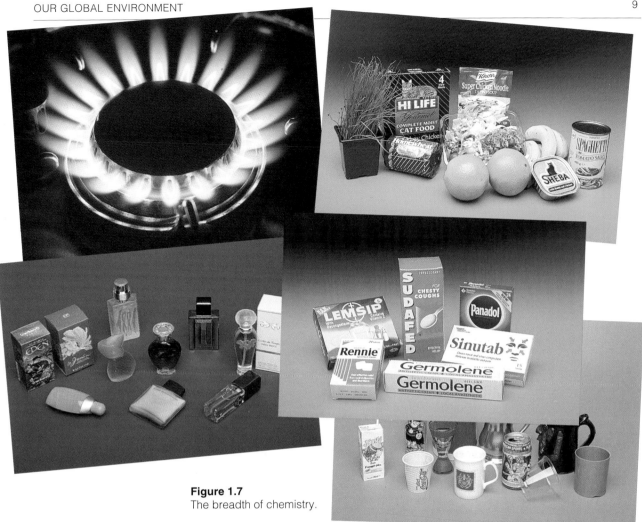

Figure 1.7
The breadth of chemistry.

discovering the way that the world is constructed; making sense of the diversity of forms, materials and colours around us; appreciating, or even participating in, the creation of materials or medicines that have never been seen before. In short, we want to develop your sense of curiosity about your surroundings. By the end of the Course, we hope that you will have been imbued with a sense of excitement and stimulated to want to learn more about these and other aspects of chemistry.

Question 1   Using information from the text or from general knowledge, list three innovations that you believe have resulted from the space programme.

Question 2   Near the beginning of Chapter 1, a number of examples of pollution were listed. Use your general knowledge to identify what were the perceived *benefits* of any one of the innovations that gave rise to this pollution as an undesirable, and often unforeseen, by-product.

You will find answers to these questions near the end of the book, starting on page 173.

Chapter 2
What is science?

There is something fascinating about science. One gets such wholesale returns of conjecture out of such a trifling investment of fact.
(Mark Twain, Life on the Mississippi, *1874)*

2.1 Arts and sciences

A major factor behind the original 'space race' that culminated in landing on the Moon was certainly a political one related to the Cold War. However, sheer curiosity undoubtedly played an important part and has continued to do so with the various probes that have been sent to explore the other planets in the Solar System (Figure 2.1). Such curiosity, whether it be about the farthest reaches of the Universe or the workings of the world around us, is *the* major driving force behind the human activity that we call science.

Curiosity about the natural world has been evident since long before the dawn of civilization. The recording of everyday events and activities in the form of cave paintings provides some of the earliest evidence (Figure 2.2). These magnificent images were created sometime during the Upper Palaeolithic period (about 35 000 to 10 000 BC) by groups of humans living a hunter–gatherer existence. Paintings such as these, discovered notably in the caves of the Dordogne in France and at Altamira in Spain, are widely regarded as the beginnings of art, but equally can be regarded as the beginnings of science, since they are thought by some to have had an instructional role:

> *Scientific illustration has its roots in the earliest endeavours of* Homo sapiens. *The great cave paintings made by our predecessors, and seen again only in recent years, have attracted attention for the beauty of their line and the balanced composition of the image. They are seen as the beginnings of Art. Yet their artistic nature is a retrospective convenience for those already tutored in the unravelling of representational and interpretative painting. To the painters of Altamira or Lascaux there was no artistic tradition with which the aesthetics of their work might meld. These images are not art, but science.*
>
> *(B. J. Ford,* Images of Science – A History of Scientific Illustration, *The British Library, 1992, p. 7)*

However, not everyone would agree with this view (Figure 2.3)!

Figure 2.1
A picture of Jupiter taken from *Voyager 1* on 1 February 1979 at a distance of 20 million miles. Two of Jupiter's four largest moons can be seen clearly, Europa near the centre with Io to the left. Also visible, beyond Io, is the Great Red Spot, a giant storm in Jupiter's atmosphere.

Figure 2.2
A cave painting depicting a pregnant mare from Lascaux in the Dordogne region of France.

"You know what our trouble is– too many artists and not enough scientists!"

Figure 2.3

Once groups of humans began to cooperate to build dwellings, to cultivate crops, and to farm animals, rather than to rely on a hunter–gatherer type of existence, observation and primitive experiment enabled improvements in the success of all these tasks to be made. This process is believed to have begun in the fertile crescent running from Israel to western Iran around 8000 BC (Figure 2.4). Observation of the pattern of the seasons, and their effect on growing crops, would have been crucial to the success of the early farmers.

The evolution of tools from simple stone implements to the use of metal, first bronze and then iron (Figure 2.5); the recording of everyday events and activities on clay tablets (Figure 2.6) and later on papyrus (Figure 2.7); and the creation of colossal constructs such as the menhirs of Brittany in France (Figure 2.8), Stonehenge (Figure 2.9), and the great Pyramids of Egypt (Figure 2.10): all these activities reveal an awareness of and a curiosity about the natural world.

upright prehistoric monumental stone

Figure 2.4
There is strong evidence that the cultivation of crops and the domestication of animals first developed in the region shaded dark green.

Figure 2.5
A selection of tools
illustrating stone age,
bronze age and iron age.

Figure 2.6 (left, middle)
A Babylonian lunar calendar, 5th century BC.

Figure 2.7 (left)
'Anubis weighs heart against Feather of Truth': from an
Egyptian Book of the Dead, 1250 BC.

Figure 2.8 (above)
Menhirs in Brittany (about 2500 BC). The alignment of these
stone megaliths near Carnac in Brittany is also thought to
indicate, as with Stonehenge, that there was a link with
astronomical observations.

Figure 2.9
Stonehenge (about 2000 BC). There is still controversy about the purpose of Stonehenge. It was almost certainly some sort of temple, but there is less agreement as to whether or not it also had an astronomical function as an observatory.

Figure 2.10
The Pyramids at Giza in Egypt. The largest, the great pyramid of King Cheops, was built around 2500 BC; a total of two million blocks of limestone, some weighing as much as 15 000 kilograms, were used in its construction. Recent research suggests that the siting of the 70 or so pyramids along the River Nile corresponds with the positions of key stars in the night sky at that time, with the size being proportional to the brightness.

Presumably, many of these activities were undertaken for specific reasons with a view initially to understanding the rhythm of nature, in order simply to improve the chance of survival against the myriad dangers to life. Many of these dangers, such as disease, or cataclysmic events such as earthquakes (Figure 2.11) or volcanic eruptions (Figure 2.12), would have causes that early humankind could not begin to fathom.

Eventually, the first relatively sophisticated societies appeared in places such as Egypt, China and Assyria. Although, for most people, everyday existence would have been harsh and allowed little or no time for leisure or contemplation, small select groups of individuals would have been allowed to pursue activities that we would regard as marking the transition between primitive societies and early civilization. Such privileged individuals would have developed skills in crafts such as decorative metalwork, for example, and others would have been allowed the freedom to investigate natural

Figure 2.11
Damage caused to a freeway in Oakland, California, during an earthquake in 1989.

Figure 2.12
Eruption of the island volcano Surtsey off the south coast of Iceland in 1964.

phenomena and to contemplate the deeper meaning of life. It was probably at this time that a distinction began to emerge between the more technical aspects of agriculture and crafts and the more aesthetic. However, this is not to imply the existence of the kind of barrier between the arts on the one hand and science and technology on the other that, unfortunately, seems to be so prevalent today (Figure 2.13).

Science as we know it was a comparatively late product of human civilization, growing out of the twin strands of craft traditions and natural philosophy. The process by which modern science evolved is admirably described by Stephen F. Mason:

Figure 2.13
Art and technology. An irrigation system in ancient Egypt as depicted in a tomb painting.

> *Prior to the modern period of history, we cannot say that there was much of a scientific tradition, distinct from the tradition of the philosophers on the one hand, and that of the craftsmen on the other. The roots of science, however, ran deep, stretching back to the period before the appearance of civilization. No matter how far back in history we go there were always some techniques, facts, and conceptions, known to craftsmen or scholars, which were scientific in character, though before modern times such knowledge in general was subordinate to the requirements of either the philosophical or the craft tradition. ...*

> *Science had its historical roots in two primary sources. Firstly, the technical tradition, in which practical experience and skills were handed on and developed from one generation to another; and secondly, the spiritual tradition, in which human aspirations and ideas were passed on and augmented. Such traditions existed before civilization appeared, if we are to judge by the continuity in the development of the tools used by the men [sic] of the stone age, and by their burial practices and cave paintings. ...in general, it was not until the late middle ages and early modern times that elements from the two traditions began to converge, and then combine, producing a new tradition, that of science.*

> (S. F. Mason, A History of the Sciences, *Collier Books, 1962, pp. 11–12)*

2.2 The scientific method

What, then, is science? How is scientific knowledge obtained? Is the method by which this happens any different from the way in which people perceive and discover the world around them in their everyday activities? Every human being learns a lot about the world without ever getting involved in 'doing science'. Most of this commonsense knowledge comes from everyday experience and is acquired over a period of years. For example, you do not need to be a scientist to know that it is not advisable to touch an object that glows red. This knowledge will have been acquired either by (painful) experience or by instruction from parents or other more experienced people.

Figure 2.14
Francis Bacon (1561–1626). Bacon was among the first to recognize the potential that science held for humanity. Primarily a philosopher rather than a practical scientist, he set out to analyse and define the scientific method so that others might apply it.

Figure 2.15
Galileo Galilei (1564–1642). Galileo was much concerned with the role of mathematics in scientific method. He also used the recently invented telescope to study the heavens, and his investigations supported the heretical Copernican theory that the Earth rotated about the Sun. For this, he was summoned in 1615 before the Inquisition and made to renounce his views. Galileo did not, however, change his opinions and continued to put forward arguments for the Copernican system. A second summons to the Inquisition in 1633 led to his confinement to a villa in Florence for the remaining nine years of his life.

However, this is not the same as understanding why a hot object glows or how the colour of an object and its temperature are related. It is in searching for answers to questions such as these that science begins. Or, put a different way, science begins when a person tries to reach beyond common experience and observation.

If you ask most people how they think scientific discoveries are made the word 'experiment' would probably be somewhere in the explanation. To many of us, it might seem almost obvious that if you want to find out about something 'scientific' then you carry out an experiment. You may think that the idea of finding things out by pushing, bending or changing something 'to see what happens' is part of natural human curiosity. It's what everyone does. Babies learn that way. If you watch young children at play you will see them experimenting by, say, banging two things together to hear the noise they make, then another pair and so on. When the noisiest or otherwise most satisfactory pair has been found then the concert begins. The child has *discovered by experiment*. That does not necessarily make him or her a scientist; there is more to science than banging bricks together! Perhaps by the end of the Course you will have an opinion on which of the following propositions is the more true: 'all children are like scientists' or 'all scientists are like children'!

Knowledge that is based on discovering things by experiment is called empirical knowledge. Modern science is founded on the **empirical approach**. However, this is a relatively recent development. From the time of the early Greek philosophers (about 600 BC) until the seventeenth century the dominant and generally accepted theories of the physical world were largely based on philosophical argument. That is not to say that the early Greek philosophers did not carry out experiments. Indeed, part of their legacy to modern science is the use of the empirical method. But the great difference between then and now was the belief that the laws of nature were discoverable by rational argument (see Box 2.1).

It was not until the 16th century that scientists such as Francis Bacon (Figure 2.14), Lord Chancellor of England under James I, and Galileo Galilei (Figure 2.15), working in Pisa, Padua and Florence, challenged this long-held view and developed what is known as the **scientific method**. Although the view expressed much later by the biologist Thomas Huxley (1825–1895), that the scientific method is 'nothing but trained and organized common sense', is an oversimplification, it contains more than a grain of truth. The great power of the scientific method lies in its rigorous and creative application.

Robert Boyle (Figure 2.16) was one of the first scientists to put into practice Bacon's ideas concerning the importance of experiment within the scientific method. Boyle's belief that experimentation must precede the formulation of a theory was conveyed in a letter to a friend:

> *But as I cultivated chemistry, not so much for itself, as for the sake of natural philosophy... so most of the experiments I devised and pursued, were generally such, as tended...to serve for foundations, and other useful materials for an experimental history of nature, on which a solid theory may in process of time be superstructed.*

(M. Boas, Robert Boyle and Seventeenth Century Chemistry, *Cambridge University Press, 1958, p. 64)*

Figure 2.16
Robert Boyle (1627–1691). As you will see in Chapter 3, Boyle's contributions marked the beginnings of modern chemical science. He also carried out important work in physics and discovered the law named after him (Boyle's law) relating the volume of a gas to its pressure.

The increased adoption of this outlook was one of the features that marked a new era in the history of physical science, a watershed now known as the Scientific Revolution.

The scientific method depends on the fundamental belief that there is an underlying pattern in nature that, by asking the right questions, can be understood. The first stage is **observation**. As we go about our everyday activities, it is difficult not to notice certain patterns or regularities. Once our curiosity has been aroused by some regularity of nature, the next stage would be to undertake more systematic observations and perhaps make some quantitative measurements. In order to guide their observations and measurements, scientists generally construct a **hypothesis**. A hypothesis is a kind of informed and, with luck, inspired guess that is put forward to account for experimental observations or known facts. But it is only a starting point for further investigations. A simple example would be to provide an explanation for why the lights in your house suddenly go out. One hypothesis would be that the main fuse had blown (or the main circuit-breaker had been triggered); a second would be that there had been a power cut. Replacing the fuse (or resetting the circuit breaker) would allow the first hypothesis to be tested, and checking to see if nearby houses were also in darkness would test the second.

Box 2.1 The Greek picture of matter

The view of matter developed by the early Greek philosophers dominated Western philosophy and science for about 2100 years. The most influential were Plato and Aristotle. Plato (427–347 BC) was born in Athens. As a young man he travelled extensively before returning to Athens to found a school, called the Academia (from which the term academic is derived). Plato rejected the world of experience and the senses in favour of a self-created world of pure thought. His view of the world was essentially a mathematical one. He believed, for example, that the planets moved in perfect circles, despite the observed irregularities in their orbits that showed these were clearly not circular. He also accepted and refined the earlier idea that all matter was made up of four elements, adding a fifth, the ether, which made up the heavens (Figure 2.17).

Plato's pupil Aristotle (384–322 BC) gave more depth to the ideas of the four earthly elements and combined this with the belief that purpose was the fundamental concept in science. However, as we shall see in Chapter 3, Plato and Aristotle disagreed about the ultimate structure of matter.

Figure 2.17
The Greek elements. In this early engraving, the two globes on which the figure is standing, one on land and the other in the sea, represent earth and water; in his hands are the elements air and fire; the heavens are composed of the fifth element, the ether.

E. J. Holmyard encapsulates the essence of Aristotle's four-element theory (Figure 2.18) in his book *Alchemy*.

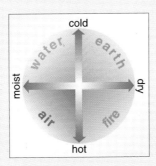

Figure 2.18
The four ancient elements, earth, air, fire and water.

The four primary qualities are the fluid (or moist), the dry, the hot, and the cold, and each element possesses two of them. Hot or cold, however, and fluid and dry, are contraries and cannot be coupled; hence the four possible combinations of them in pairs are: hot and dry, assigned to fire; hot and fluid, assigned to air; cold and fluid, assigned to water; cold and dry, assigned to earth.

In each element, one quality predominates over the other; in earth, dryness; in water, cold; in air, fluidity; and in fire, heat. None of the four elements is unchangeable; they may pass into one another through the medium of that quality which they possess in common; thus fire can become air through the medium of heat, air can become water through the medium of fluidity, and so on. Two elements taken together may become a third by removing one quality from each, subject to the limitation that this process must not leave two identical or contrary qualities; thus fire and water, by parting with the dry and cold qualities could give rise to earth. In all these changes it is only the 'form' that alters; the prime matter of which the elements are made never changes, however diverse and numerous the changes of form may be.

(E. J. Holmyard, Alchemy, Penguin, 1957, pp. 21–23)

On the basis of the results from such further investigations, we then try to formulate a rule or a set of rules that represent or simulate the behaviour of the system being studied. In other words, we try to construct a **model**. In constructing a model, we generally concentrate on replicating just the particular features in which we are interested. So, by its very nature, a model is often a very much simplified description of the system under investigation. This process, the construction of a model from statements describing individual phenomena, is called **induction**. Induction requires a degree of imagination or creativity in order to make the necessary connections between the initial observations and other knowledge, which allows an appropriate model to be devised (this process often calls for what is known as lateral thinking). Developing this skill is an important part of any scientist's training.

Scientific models are often conceptual, and not physical in the sense that a model car or aeroplane is a scaled-down replica of the real thing. However, in chemistry we do frequently make use of physical models constructed with a model kit that bears a more than passing resemblance to a box of Lego! You will be introduced to the model kit later in this Book, and subsequently make use of it throughout the Course.

Constructing a model has a number of advantages over the description of the individual observations: (i) it is much more concise, allowing many observations to be encompassed by one description; (ii) it allows us to concentrate on a particular aspect of a problem by using a simplified model that only contains those features of interest; and (iii) it allows predictions to be made about particular individual events. This latter process is called **deduction**, and is essentially the opposite of induction. This is crucial to the scientific method because it allows the general statement to be tested by carrying out further experiments.

If an experiment is devised or an observation made based on some prediction of the model and the result is not in agreement with the model, then it is the latter that has to be discarded (or at least modified) not the experimental results that have to be ignored. This reliance on experimental results presupposes that the experiment is a '**fair test**': we shall examine just what constitutes a fair test in more detail later in the Course.

As we have seen, the first step in developing a model is the framing of a hypothesis. We put forward a hypothesis to help us to decide what experiments to do so that we can discover more about something. More often than not, the hypothesis will then need to be modified in the light of the results. We can see how the process works in the following (hypothetical!) example.

Suppose that we are investigating to what extent different substances dissolve in water, that is their solubility. We know that sugar readily dissolves in water so we say it is soluble. Table salt also dissolves in water so it is soluble too. A sloppy chemist might frame a hypothesis based on just those two experimental observations. The hypothesis could be 'all white solids are soluble in water.' Let's look at that hypothesis in more detail. We'll try a different way of looking at it.

The following is a dialogue based loosely on the type that Socrates, Plato's teacher, used to illustrate his arguments. His arguments were claimed to be based on pure reason. Here we make use of the dialogue form to illustrate a modern scientific argument. Let's imagine that the dialogue is between two fictitious people, Charlotte, a scientist, and David, a non-scientist. Where you can, try to take part in the dialogue by thinking of your own reply to each question raised before reading Charlotte or David's response.

Charlotte   The hypothesis is, 'all white solids dissolve in water.' What do think about that hypothesis?

David   It's nonsense.

Charlotte   That is not a sufficient answer. Why is it nonsense? Can you demonstrate, or prove, that it is not a general law?

David   Yes, it's easily shown to be a false hypothesis. The white cliffs of Dover are very solid and very white and very insoluble in water.

Charlotte   How do you know the white cliffs of Dover are insoluble in water?

David   Are you serious?

Charlotte   I'm a scientist, of course I'm serious. Try to answer the question.

David   Well, they are constantly in contact with water and they haven't disappeared yet. When any part of the cliff does disappear it's probably the result of mechanical erosion rather than solubility.

Charlotte   Now your argument uses the word 'probably'. That still isn't sufficient to disprove the hypothesis. You have to set out to test it in a controlled and repeatable way. That's what the scientific method tells us.

David   All right. But it also tells us that a proper hypothesis is one that is testable. The 'all white solids are soluble' hypothesis is very difficult to test. Look at the way in which the hypothesis is framed. It's not specific enough.

Charlotte   It seems fairly specific to me. All it needs for it to be tested is to decide whether a given substance is soluble or not.

David   But it doesn't specify a quantity or proportion of the solid that will dissolve, or the amount of water that is needed. It doesn't specify a time-scale. No-one could say with certainty that, given millions of years, some solid would not dissolve, even though no dissolution is observable over hours or days.

Charlotte   All right. Let's reformulate the hypothesis. How about 'all white solids are soluble in water to the extent of at least one gram in one litre at twenty degrees Celsius within ten minutes.' Now can you test it?

David   Yes, I think I could test it by experiment as follows. I would take a white solid that I believe to be insoluble in water, such as blackboard chalk. I would weigh an amount greater than one gram and add it to a litre of water at twenty degrees Celsius. After ten minutes I would remove the solid, and after drying it I would weigh it again. If it has lost less than one gram in weight, then less than one gram must have dissolved in the water. The hypothesis is therefore disproved. If more than a gram has been lost it must have dissolved, so the hypothesis still stands. I would have to try again with another white solid until I found one that is insoluble.

Charlotte   Yes, that would work. In this case you would find that the chalk does not dissolve to a measurable extent in water and so that easily disproves the hypothesis. You are starting to think like a scientist. You have shown me that you can disprove a hypothesis. Do you think that any hypothesis can be proved?

David   That might not be so easy. If a hypothesis attempts to frame a general rule or law then I could not possibly test every possible example.

Charlotte   Quite so. It is usually accepted that a hypothesis cannot be proved. There may always be an experiment that would disprove it. We accept that a hypothesis is valid until an experiment disproves it. Does that suggest anything about the nature of scientific knowledge?

David   It suggests that there can be no certainties, no absolutes in science. But isn't science bulging with laws and definite relationships between things?

Charlotte   Yes it is, but they are all provisional. We have to be ready for any of our laws to be invalidated at any time. Science will never be complete. We are always trying to edge closer to the 'truth' but like the rainbow's end it's always just in front of us.

Not all hypotheses are as easily disproved as the one we have just been discussing. If a hypothesis is successful and repeated experiments suggest that it is true, then it is promoted and becomes a **scientific law**. A law is a summary of experience based on a large number of observations and experiments over a wide range of individual cases to which there is no known exception. Remember that a law has still not been proved, but it has stood the test of experiment and has not so far been shown to be wrong or inadequate. A hypothesis such as the one 'all white solids are soluble in water', which does not stand up to experimental investigation, is said to be *refuted*. One that passes all the experimental tests thrown at it is said to be *verified*.

Having made the observations and carried out the experiments, the results of which are summarized in the statement of a law, scientists try to formulate an explanation for the results based on a small number of fundamental ideas. Such an explanation is called a **theory**. A good theory has predictive value as it tells you what should happen in a given set of circumstances. The best theories also tell you which things won't happen. It has been said that the more things a theory forbids to happen the better it is. When scientists examine a theory, the best experiments are those designed to try to disprove it rather than prove it. Remember, no experiment can be designed to prove the correctness of a theory; the best that can be done is to carry out experiments that produce evidence in support. A real test of a theory is an attempt to disprove it.

So science is made up of a set of unprovable theories. Isn't that a rather weak position to be in? Yes and no is the answer to that question. Yes, it is weak because we can never know for certain that the results of any new experiment will turn out as predicted. But it is strong because in science in general, and chemistry in particular, the success rate of predictions is very high. Our theories are powerful enough for us to develop rational experiments with a high degree of success. Not many scientists would want 100% success in experiments anyway, because the challenge and the excitement would have completely disappeared.

It may appear from what has been presented so far that science is now a perfectly logical and rational activity. To some extent we like to think that this is so, but chance often plays an important part (Figure 2.19) and the role of the imagination and of creative thinking should not be underrated. The most

'That's Dr Arnold Moore. He's conducting an experiment to test the theory that most great scientific discoveries were hit on by accident.'

Figure 2.19

innovative advances are often those where a wild idea or an unexpected side result has been chased, perhaps with no particular purpose other than to find out what happens. The discovery of penicillin by Alexander Fleming (1881–1955) is a good example of the latter.

Fleming was engaged in a search for an effective antiseptic substance that would be able to kill the bacteria that cause disease. The antiseptics then available did more harm than good for deep wounds as they damaged the surrounding tissues. Quite by chance, he noticed that some mould growing in a dish had the effect of killing bacteria. His careful observation and his decision to follow up these unexpected results led to the discovery of the family of antibiotics now known as beta-lactams. But this epoch-making discovery was made only because Fleming's experience enabled him to recognize and appreciate the significance of his unexpected observation. A good scientist is one who retains an open mind and is always prepared for the unexpected.

The experimental basis of the scientific method means that there are definite limits to the matters that come within the orbit of science. The aim of science is to be objective, and so it should not be concerned with making value judgements: it is not a 'scientific' matter to decide whether or not a painting, or a piece of music, or a landscape is beautiful. Neither is it part of science to make judgements as to the morality of particular actions or events, such as the use of nuclear weapons. However, this is not to say that scientists *as people* cannot appreciate the beauty of art or music, or that they do not use their scientific knowledge to make moral judgements. Further, science can provide the necessary information to allow others, whether scientists or non-scientists, to make informed judgements. But such matters are not the concern of science itself.

You should now carry out the exercise in Activity 1, which will give you some experience in scientific observation. When you have done this, read the comments on this Activity in the section Comments on Activities, starting on p. 171.

Activity 1 A burning match

You will need a box of (wooden) matches and an old glass tumbler of cold water. With these everyday objects, you will be able to observe a chemical change.

1 Take a wooden match and strike it. Allow it to burn about halfway down then blow it out. Write down in your notebook as many observations as you can about what happened during the burning process.

2 Examine the black residue. Again write down what you see.

3 Now light another match and hold it a few centimetres beneath the tumbler containing cold water. Let the match burn for as long as possible before extinguishing it. Examine the bottom of the tumbler. Write down your observations.

Describe your observations as clearly and accurately as you can. Include as much detail as you think you need to help you to recall everything after months or years!

2.3 Science and technology

For many people, the differences between science and technology are blurred or even non-existent. Such a confusion is apparent in the anonymous observation that 'One humiliating thing about science is that it is gradually filling our homes with appliances smarter than we are!' Even for those with a scientific or technological background, it is not always clear whether a particular development or discovery is scientific or technological. To some extent, the language used indicates which is involved: we generally talk about scientific *discoveries* and technological *developments*. But there is a continuous spectrum from topics that are purely scientific to applications that are essentially wholly technological, with the majority in between exhibiting aspects of both. However, it is still possible to identify whether some advance is predominantly scientific or predominantly technological.

Consider the three discoveries or developments described in Activity 2, and decide from your own experience whether you would class them as predominantly scientific or predominantly technological. They are based on newspaper articles, and so depend only on general knowledge to understand them sufficiently to answer this question. When you have done this you should read the comments on this Activity at the end of the book.

Activity 2   Science or technology?

TECH

(a) An oil company in its geological surveys of an existing oilfield found that it extended further than was previously thought. In order to reach the oil, rather than build a new oil-rig, with its associated costs and environmental implications, a novel method was developed that allowed access to the newly discovered oil from the existing platform. This involved the use of new techniques to allow drilling at such a long distance and a new type of drilling head that could be tilted under the control of a gyroscope. The drill started off vertically, but was then turned until it was almost horizontal.

(b) Collaboration between a multinational company and a university laboratory made a breakthrough that opens the way for a new generation of computers able to learn to recognize patterns much faster than existing ones. They incorporate so-called 'neural networks', that is an array of linked microprocessors that mimics the human brain. A limit on the number of electrical connections between conventional devices is set by the need to keep the signals separate otherwise they interfere with one another. However, academics at Trinity College Dublin had developed new microprocessor devices that operate at very high

SCIENCE
& TECH

speed, based on a particularly uniform type of gallium arsenide (a semiconductor material used to make computer chips) rather than the 'traditional' silicon. These allow the signals to be transmitted using light. Because light beams can intersect one another without interference, by using these devices it has proved possible for researchers at Hitachi Dublin laboratories to make the very large number of complex interconnections needed to create the neural network.

(c) Researchers at Aberdeen University and the Hebrew University, Jerusalem, discovered a hitherto unknown

SCIENCE

substance produced by the brain which has effects similar to those produced by THC (tetrahydrocannabinol), the active ingredient in hashish (cannabis). They have named the new chemical anandamide. Tests have confirmed that anandamide is biologically active when injected into animals. It is hoped that the discovery will help to provide clues to certain mental disorders and possibly even to throw some light on the processes by which we learn and memorize information.

From one point of view, pure scientific research could be regarded as a very selfish activity. The pursuit of knowledge of natural phenomena simply because of curiosity without any thought of direct applications would seem at first sight a luxury that, in these days of market forces, cannot be afforded. Yet, looking back over recent history at many of the discoveries that have transformed our lives, such as the discovery of penicillin and related antibiotics, the development of the laser, and the discovery of polythene and nylon, we see that they have all been largely the result of scientific curiosity, although it must be said that the work leading to the discovery of polythene and nylon was carried out in industrial research laboratories. By its very nature, the results of exploration of the unknown cannot be foreseen, and research directed to a particular application is not guaranteed to produce major discoveries.

As we saw in Section 2.1, technology as an activity is ancient, and predates the study of science. It began as a trial-and-error approach to solving particular problems, with new technical advances being handed down by craft workers from one generation to the next. The relationship between science and technology is symbiotic: on the one hand, these traditions provide a basis for the development of scientific ideas, and on the other, the application of scientific principles to what we would now regard as technological problems happened at an early stage.

living together to mutual advantage

One famous example involved the Greek philosopher and scientist, Archimedes (287–212 BC). Nearly everyone is familiar with the story that Archimedes had a brilliant idea while bathing one day (Figure 2.20) and was so delighted that he ran home naked crying out 'Eureka!', which is Greek for 'I have found it!'. However, rather fewer people are aware of the reason why Archimedes was so excited.

Figure 2.20
Eureka! An artist's impression of Archimedes at the point of his famous discovery.

According to legend, a goldsmith, in making a crown commissioned by Hiero, king of Syracuse, was accused of replacing some of the gold that the king had given him by silver, a less valuable metal. However, because of the ornate shape of the crown, proving it was no easy matter. Archimedes, puzzling over the problem while bathing, suddenly realized that the volume of water displaced on getting into the pool was equal to the volume of that part of himself immersed in water. This provided the clue which enabled him to show clearly that the goldsmith had indeed defrauded the King and replaced some of the gold with a less dense metal (see Box 2.2). Until Archimedes' time, the Greeks had assumed that the weight of an object (strictly mass, as we shall see in Section 6.1) was simply proportional to its volume.

Box 2.2 Eureka!

The following account of Archimedes' discovery is by the Roman architect Vitruvius (translated by F. Granger), and was written some two hundred years later, so it may not be completely true. However, Archimedes' own writings contain some evidence to support it.

Hiero was greatly exalted in the regal power at Syracuse, and after his victories he determined to set up in a certain temple a crown vowed to the immortal gods. He let out the execution as far as the craftsman's wages were concerned, and weighed the gold out to the contractor to an exact amount. At the appointed time the man presented the work finely wrought for the king's acceptance, and

appeared to have furnished the weight of the crown to scale.

However, information was laid that gold had been withdrawn, and that the same amount of silver had been added in the making of the crown. Hiero was indignant that he had been made light of, and failing to find a method by which he might detect the theft, asked Archimedes to undertake the investigation. While Archimedes was considering the matter, he happened to go to the baths. When he went down into the bathing pool he observed that the amount of water which flowed outside the pool was equal to the amount of his body that was immersed. Since this fact indicated the method of explaining the case, he did not linger, but moved with delight he leapt out of the pool, and going home naked, cried aloud that he

had found exactly what he was seeking. For as he ran he shouted in Greek: eureka, eureka.

Then, following up his discovery, he is said to have taken two masses of the same weight as the crown, one of gold and the other of silver. When he had done this, he filled a large vessel to the brim with water, into which he dropped the mass of silver. The amount of this when let down into the water corresponded to the overflow of water. So he removed the metal and filled in by measure the amount by which the water was diminished, so that it was level with the brim as before. In this way he discovered what weight of silver corresponded to a given measure of water.

After this experiment he then dropped a mass of gold in like manner into the full vessel and

removed it. Again he added water by measure, and discovered that there was not so much water; and this corresponded to the lessened quantity [volume] of the same weight of gold compared with the same weight of silver. He then let down the crown itself into the vase after filling the vase with water, and found that more water flowed into the space left by the crown than into the space left by a mass of gold of the same weight. And so from the fact that there was more water in the case of the crown than in the mass of gold, he calculated and detected the mixture of the silver with the gold, and the fraud of the contractor.

(Translated by the author in F. Granger, *Vitruvius on Architecture, Vol. II,* Harvard University Press, 1934)

In modern times, the relationship between science and technology has become ever closer, and many new scientific discoveries have been made possible only by technological developments. A striking example of this is the construction of the large particle accelerator at the CERN laboratories in Geneva, Switzerland (Figure 2.21), used to investigate the ultimate structure of matter. In this accelerator, or synchrotron, particles are accelerated to near the speed of light and then allowed to collide with a stationary target or with another beam of particles travelling in the opposite direction.

The technology required to build the synchrotron in the first place is remarkable, given that it is built in an underground tunnel that forms a huge ring twenty-seven kilometres around the circumference. The project involved positioning large electromagnets, each weighing five tonnes (one tonne = one thousand kilograms), to an accuracy of one millimetre. To avoid unwanted collisions, all the air has to be removed from the interior of the accelerator, and in operation as the particles accelerate, the strength of the magnetic field used to keep the beam travelling in a circular path has to be

(a)

(b)

Figure 2.21
The CERN LEP (large electron-positron) particle accelerator in Geneva, Switzerland: (a) aerial view of site: the larger of the superimposed circles shows the location of the tunnel; (b) cross-section of tunnel during construction.

increased at a very precise rate. Clearly, without very advanced technology, the scientific discoveries of new fundamental particles that have been achieved at the CERN laboratories could not have happened.

Equally, the innovations described at the start of this Section depended on earlier scientific discoveries for their development. Other, more familiar, instances readily come to mind. For example, the invention of the laser resulted from purely scientific investigations. Yet that one discovery has given rise to a whole range of applications: improved music reproduction by means of compact discs (CDs); the use of CD-ROMs (Read-Only Memory) for the storage of vast amounts of data; the ability to produce high-quality text and graphics using laser printers; and the use of laser scanners to read barcodes.

Other, perhaps less well known, uses of lasers include:

● The accurate measurement of the distance from the Earth to the Moon by bouncing a laser beam off a reflector placed on the surface of the Moon by the Apollo astronauts (Figure 2.22);

Figure 2.22
A reflector placed on the Moon by the *Apollo 11* astronauts.

● Mapping the Earth's gravitational attraction by similarly reflecting a laser beam from a satellite (Figure 2.23);

● The use of lasers capable of producing pulses of light lasting less than a million millionth of a second (Figure 2.24) to study extremely fast chemical processes such as those that take place during photosynthesis (the conversion by plants of water and carbon dioxide into carbohydrate brought about by sunlight);

● Fibre-optics communication links that allow the transmission of thousands of telephone conversations as well as computer data and television signals over long distances (Figure 2.25).

Perhaps the best definition of pure science as distinct from technology is encapsulated in the famous statement of the great scientist Sir Isaac Newton at the end of his life:

> *I do not know what I may appear to the world, but to myself I seem to have been only like a boy playing on the sea-shore, and diverting myself in now and then finding a smoother pebble or a prettier shell than ordinary, whilst the great ocean of truth lay all undiscovered before me.*

(R. L. Weber, A Random Walk in Science, *edited by E. Mendoza, The Institute of Physics, London, 1973, p. 203)*

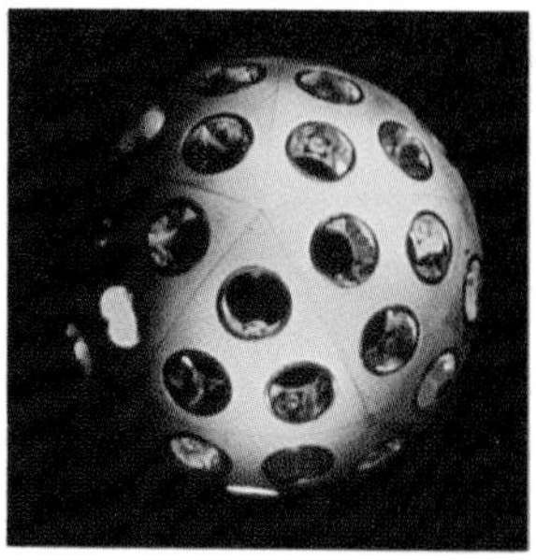

Figure 2.23
The European Space Agency's satellite Starlette. Though small, it is extremely heavy, and responds to minor variations in the Earth's gravitational attraction. The consequent small changes in its orbit can be easily determined by measuring the time taken for a laser beam to be reflected back to Earth.

Figure 2.24
Laser capable of producing light pulses of less than a million millionth of a second long.

Figure 2.25
Fibre-optics communications link.

Summary of Chapter 2

Curiosity about the natural world has been evident since long before the dawn of civilization. Early humans left records of their way of life in the form of artefacts, such as cave paintings, tools, carvings and monuments.

With the domestication of animals and the successful farming of crops, relatively sophisticated societies began to appear. This provided sufficient food so that certain privileged individuals would have been allowed the freedom to pursue various crafts and to engage in philosophy. The combination of the craft traditions and natural philosophy gave rise to knowledge and activities that we would now regard as being scientific in character.

Knowledge that is based on discovery by experiment is called empirical. Modern science is founded on the empirical approach. However, from about 600 BC, the dominant theories of the physical world were those put forward by the early Greek philosophers. These were based on the belief that the laws of nature were discoverable by rational argument rather than by observation and experiment. It was not until the late 16th or early 17th centuries that this view began to change and the modern scientific method emerged.

The scientific method begins with observations. In order to guide their observations and measurements, scientists generally formulate a hypothesis. A hypothesis is a kind of guess put forward to account for experimental observations or known facts, but it is only a starting point for further investigations. On the basis of the results of these investigations, a model would be constructed, that is a rule or a set of rules that represent or simulate the behaviour of the system being studied.

If a hypothesis is successful and repeated experiments do not disprove it, then it becomes a law. A law is a summary of experience based on a large number of observations and experiments to which there is no known exception. Scientists then try to formulate an explanation for the results based on a small number of fundamental ideas. Such an explanation is called a theory. No experiment can be designed to prove the correctness of a theory; the best that can be done is to carry out experiments that produce evidence in support.

Science, then, involves a set of unprovable theories. This may seem unsatisfactory, because some future experiment may disprove one or more theories. However, current theories are powerful enough to allow predictions to be made with a high degree of success. If the theories were always completely successful, scientific investigation would cease!

The experimental basis of the scientific method means that there are definite limits to the matters that come within the orbit of science. Science aims to be objective and so it should not be concerned with making value judgements.

Though often confused with one another in people's minds, science and technology are distinct activities. However, they are interrelated to a greater or lesser degree and are mutually supportive: technological innovations rely on scientific discoveries; conversely, scientific discovery is increasingly dependent on the application of technological developments and can, indeed, be stimulated by them.

Question 3 Step back in time and attempt to interpret your observations during the burning match experiment in terms of the theory of the four elements: air, earth, fire and water.

Question 4 Classify the following early activities as craft, technology, science, philosophy, or some combination of these.

(a) The development of the irrigation system illustrated in Figure 2.13.

(b) Attempts to make gold by melting together copper, tin, lead and iron, whitening the surface with arsenic or mercury vapour to take on the appearance of silver then seeding with a little pure gold.

(c) Investigations into the development of chick embryos by early Greek physicians around the 5th century BC, which involved placing 20 eggs under hens and opening one egg each day to observe the internal changes until one of the eggs hatched.

(d) The devising of a model of the Universe by the Greek astronomer Apollonius around 200 BC, in which the observed movements of the planets could be accounted for if each moved in an epicycle, that is a circle the centre of which moved along another circle centred on the Earth.

(e) The production of an ornate bronze drinking vessel.

(f) The production by the Greek astronomer Hipparchus of a catalogue of stars, classifying each according to its brightness.

Question 5 In the following, distinguish the scientific and/or technological aspects from those that are neither scientific nor technological.

(a) The development of new dyes for use in artists' paints.

(b) The production between 1802 and 1816 by a Frenchman, Pierre-Joseph Redouté, of a book containing 486 carefully drawn pictures of lilies in full colour.

(c) The establishment of the Joint European Torus (JET) research project in 1978 at Culham, in Oxfordshire, to investigate the use of nuclear fusion for power generation.

(d) The construction of the THORP plant, opened in 1994, for reprocessing nuclear fuel at Sellafield in Cumbria.

(e) The cleaning and restoration of Michelangelo's paintings on the ceiling of the Sistine Chapel in the Vatican, Rome carried out over the period 1980–1994.

Question 6 You are no doubt familiar with the concept of a pendulum from their use in grandfather and other large clocks. For scientific studies, a pendulum is often made by fixing a length of string or wire to a suspension point and attaching some small heavy object at the other end. This latter is often called the pendulum 'bob'. If a pendulum is allowed to swing, the time it takes to return to the same position and moving in the same direction is called the period of swing (Figure 2.26). Studies have shown that the period of swing of such a pendulum does not depend on the angle through which the pendulum swings (called its

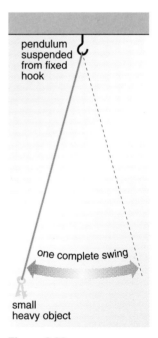

Figure 2.26
A pendulum suspended from a fixed hook.

amplitude), so the period does not change as the pendulum 'runs down'. Suggest a hypothesis about the relationship you might expect between the period of swing and (i) the length of the pendulum, and (ii) the mass of the pendulum bob. Then briefly outline how you would test your hypothesis.

Question 7   Distinguish between the scientific and technological aspects of the following news items.

(a) The Upper Atmosphere Research Satellite (UARS) was launched in September, 1991. UARS not only allows the measurement of ozone levels in the atmosphere but also provides three-dimensional maps of the chemicals that control ozone concentration. The satellite carries nine instruments to measure 16 of the ingredients at altitudes of between six and fifty miles.

(b) Implants made of titanium, a light-weight but very strong metal, are now being used to attach replacement teeth. The implants are drilled into the jawbone where they bond to the living bone. Several months later, connectors are inserted followed by the replacement teeth.

(c) In late 1988, a new artificial sweetener known as acesulfame K, said to be 200 times sweeter than sugar, was approved for use in the United States by the Food and Drug Administration. The new sweetener, claimed to be more stable than its competitors aspartame and saccharin, was already in use in Europe. It is expected to play a substantial role in combating obesity.

(d) A heat reservoir that warms and demists a frozen car almost instantly was introduced by Saab as an optional extra for its 1993 models. A thermal accumulator stores waste heat from the engine for up to a week. It relies for its operation on a heat exchanger containing the substance barium hydroxide, which melts to a liquid at 78 °C. Because this process requires a lot of heat, a large amount of heat is then given out as the barium hydroxide solidifies.

Chapter 3
Science and its
sub-divisions

The explosive growth of scientific information since the 17th century meant that scientists could no longer hope to be aware of, much less study in depth, the whole of science. Specialization began and led to the eventual emergence of the major scientific disciplines of biology, chemistry, geology and physics. This trend of increasing specialization has continued to the present day, such that any modern scientist, a chemist, for example, will be expert in just one small area of chemistry and will usually attempt to keep abreast of developments only in related fields.

This trend of specialization has to some extent been counteracted by the development of fields at the interface between different disciplines as subject areas in their own right. For example, the boundary between chemistry and biology has given rise to the subject of biochemistry, in recent years an extremely fruitful area of scientific study; other subject areas involving principles and methods of two or more of the traditional subjects are molecular biology, geochemistry, geophysics, and materials science. In this Chapter we shall look at these various disciplines and sub-disciplines.

3.1 Physics

Perhaps the earliest scientific studies would be regarded today as being part of the subject area we know as **physics**. Physics deals with the study of matter and energy from the very large to the very small: the subject of astronomy and questions such as the origins of the Universe at one extreme, to the very building blocks of matter, the fundamental particles that make up everything in the Universe at the other. Subjects studied by those scientists who regard themselves as physicists include electricity and magnetism; heat, light and sound; and the forces between objects, including gravity, and their resulting motion.

Although much of the work of the early Greeks, such as Archimedes, may be thought of as physics, their investigations were primarily driven by philosophical considerations. It wasn't until much later, with experiments by Galileo Galilei (Figure 2.17) designed to investigate the laws governing a falling object, that the study of physics as we know it is thought by many to have begun. Galileo was probably the first to apply strictly the modern scientific method based on experimentation (Figure 3.1). He made the crucial distinction between asking the question *how* did an object fall and the question *why* did an object fall. This latter question is now more properly regarded as the concern of philosophy. The historical link remains however in some University departments, where the title professor of natural philosophy is still used for the professor of physics.

Figure 3.1
The Leaning Tower of Pisa. According to legend Galileo, who studied and taught for a time at the University of Pisa, demonstrated his discovery that all bodies fall with the same acceleration by dropping a bullet and a cannon ball from the top of the Leaning Tower. The story is probably apocryphal, and Galileo actually carried out his investigations by rolling spheres down an inclined surface.

Figure 3.2
Isaac Newton (1642–1727).
Newton is undoubtedly one of
the greatest scientists to have
lived. One of the most famous
stories in all science concerns
the observation of a falling
apple by Newton, which led
him to develop his theory of
gravitation. Newton's great
contributions to science were
recognized in his own lifetime
and he was rewarded by
being made Director of the
Mint in 1699, and was given a
knighthood in 1703. He also
served in Parliament and was
President of the Royal Society
from 1703 until his death.

Galileo's studies provided the groundwork for one of the greatest scientists of all time, Isaac Newton (Figure 3.2). His investigations were wide-ranging and resulted in a series of epoch-making discoveries that marked the birth of modern physics. He discovered the Law of Gravitation which was to stand unmodified until Einstein's General Theory of Relativity. His investigation of the properties of light and its interaction with matter have survived to this day as the foundation of the science of optics. His formulation of the three Laws of Motion that carry his name has constituted the foundation of the calculations necessary for the entire space programme. And the mathematical technique of calculus that he developed is still routinely used for solving many problems. Had Newton been working in the 20th century, there is little doubt that each one of these discoveries on its own would have merited the award of a Nobel prize!

Physics deals generally with matter, energy and motion, and could be regarded therefore as embracing the whole of science. The famous scientist Lord Rutherford is reported to have joked that 'All science is either physics or stamp collecting!' But there are areas that physicists do not regard as being their territory. The transformation of one substance into another is not the concern of physicists but rather of chemists. The application of the principles of physics to natural processes occurring on the surface and within the body of the Earth is regarded as being the domain of the interdisciplinary subject geophysics, which is perhaps closer to geology than to physics. And physics is generally concerned only with inanimate matter; living matter and the energy changes associated with life are the concern of biology. However, the interdisciplinary subject of biophysics, in which the principles and methods of physics are applied to living systems, is of increasing importance.

3.2 Biology

The concerns of **biology** are much more easily defined than those of physics: biology is concerned with all living things. However, such a definition begs the question as to how we recognize life. One dictionary definition is that life is the property that distinguishes the living from the dead, and dead is in turn defined as being deprived of life. These circular definitions are clearly inadequate, and perhaps the simplest satisfactory definition would be that only a living organism is able to reproduce itself.

Modern animal biology can be said to have begun around Galileo's time, in the context of medical studies. Andreas Vesalius (1514–1564), professor of medicine at Padua, was one of the first to use the technique of dissection on corpses to study human anatomy, and he produced a textbook advocating this method of investigation. He discovered that the body is made up of several subsystems, each with its own function. He also went on to develop the comparative approach to this aspect of biology, by studying other animals to work out the purpose of each of the human subsystems. A similar approach was adopted by the English physician William Harvey (Figure 3.3), who discovered the circulation of the blood in humans, and showed that the heart is essentially a pump.

Figure 3.3
William Harvey (1578–1657).
Harvey studied medicine at
Cambridge University and
then Padua in Italy where he
also came under the
influence of Galileo. He
devoted his whole life to
studying the structure and
function of the heart and the
circulation of the blood, using
the technique of dissection
advocated by Vesalius.

Another important development was the use of the microscope, thereby enabling scientists to extend their sense of sight to study microorganisms.

One of the first to do so was the Dutchman, Antony van Leeuwenhoek (Figure 3.4), who used a microscope to inspect cloth in his job in a drapery. In his scientific studies he discovered bacteria, sperm and the eggs they fertilized, and the cellular structure of the majority of living things.

Given the huge number of species on Earth and the many different levels of study that are possible, from the study of groups of animals down to the chemical changes that occur in the various processes involved in metabolism, biology includes a large number of subject areas. Indeed, a more appropriate term to embrace such a variety is **biological sciences**, to contrast with the study of inanimate matter, which is the preserve of the **physical sciences** such as physics and chemistry.

However, there is inevitably an area of overlap between the two where the distinctions become blurred and which is the domain of the relatively new subjects of **biochemistry** and **molecular biology**. Biochemistry really took off following the epoch-making discovery of the double helix structure of DNA by James Watson and Francis Crick in 1953 (Figure 3.5) and the consequent deciphering of the genetic code. The subsequent growth of biochemistry and biophysics, in which the methods and approaches of chemistry and physics respectively are applied to the study of biological systems, has been explosive, a fact emphasized by the award in alternate years of the Nobel Prize in Chemistry for work that is strictly in biochemistry and molecular biology. In fact, one of the largest international projects within science at the present time is the attempt to map the entire genetic structure of humans, the so-called human genome (Figure 3.6).

Figure 3.4
Antony van Leeuwenhoek (1632–1723). Leeuwenhoek was able to use his microscope to see the blood passing through the capillaries in the tails of tadpoles and the foot of a frog, providing final confirmation of the mechanism of the circulation of the blood. Harvey had speculated that the blood flows from the arteries to the veins, but had been unable to see the very small capillaries that provide the pathway by which this is achieved.

Figure 3.5
James Watson and Francis Crick at Cambridge University in the 1950s. They, together with the crystallographer Maurice Wilkins, were awarded the Nobel Prize for Medicine in 1962.

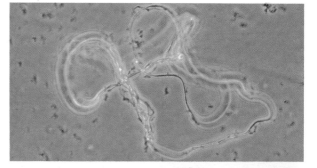

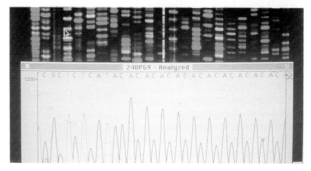

Figure 3.6
Mapping the 100 000 genes that constitute the human genome: (top) an electron micrograph of strands of human DNA; (above) the result of analysis of a section of human DNA indicating the sequence of the four building blocks of which it is made.

Figure 3.7
Abraham Gottlob Werner
(1749–1817). Werner began
his career working at the
ironworks in Saxony run by
his father. In 1775, he
secured an appointment at
the Freiburg School of
Mining. During his 42 years
there, Werner's expertise as
a mineralogist and his skill
as a teacher became widely
recognized. Acknowledged
to be the foremost geologist
of the time, he transformed
the little known institute into
a renowned centre of
scientific excellence.

Figure 3.8
James Hutton (1726–1797).
Hutton obtained a degree in
medicine from the
University of Leiden in
Holland in 1749. He then
returned to his native
Scotland and, after a period
as a farmer, moved to
Edinburgh in 1768 where he
spent the rest of his life. It
was there that he undertook
the geological studies
which eventually gave rise
to his *Theory of the Earth*.

3.3 Geology

Whereas biology is concerned with living organisms on Earth, **geology** is the scientific discipline that has as its province the Earth's physical environment, its origins and evolution. In recent times, there has also been an increasing interest in the geology of meteorites, the Moon, and other planets. Geology has its origins in the study of rocks and minerals. One of the founding figures of modern geology was Abraham Gottlob Werner (Figure 3.7) who introduced the idea that rock layers could be produced by the laying down and compaction of rock particles produced by erosion from pre-existing rock formations. This radical view conflicted with the view popular until then that all rocks arose through volcanic eruptions to produce what are now known as igneous rocks. Werner's view that the majority of rock formations were sedimentary in origin was overly simplistic, but he made important contributions to the methods of geology.

Another key figure in the emergence of modern geology was James Hutton (Figure 3.8) who, in his book *Theory of the Earth*, put forward the view known as 'Uniformitarianism'. This states that geological activity is constantly occurring and that by examining existing rock formations and the effects of processes such as earthquakes and volcano eruptions, the processes that took place earlier in the Earth's history could be inferred, an approach that Hutton encapsulated as 'the present is the key to the past'.

The boundaries of geology have expanded in recent years to embrace studies of: the composition of the Earth, both its surface and interior, the subject known as **geochemistry**; the Earth's physical behaviour, including its magnetic properties, the gradual movement of continents (plate tectonics), and such catastrophic events as earthquakes and volcanic eruptions (geophysics); the composition and motions of the atmosphere (atmospheric sciences) and of the oceans (oceanography). With this expansion has come a new name, that of the **Earth sciences**, as a more appropriate description of the subject.

3.4 Chemistry

For many people, **chemistry** is the most mysterious of all the scientific disciplines. Dealing as it does with the composition of materials and the transformation of one material into another with quite different properties, it seemed like magic to many early scientists. From about 600 BC until the 17th century, the dominant and generally accepted theories of the constitution of matter were based on philosophical argument (Section 2.2). These theories were not empirical but were inspired by the Greek rational view of Nature. From about the 12th century AD, an all-embracing obsession was alchemy, in which one of the principal aims was to change other metals into gold. However, it is a common misunderstanding that alchemy was concerned only with the search for methods of producing gold (Figure 3.9). A more accurate picture of alchemy is seen from the definition framed by H. J. Sheppard and published in the Journal for the History of Alchemy and Chemistry, *Ambix*:

> *Alchemy is a cosmic art by which parts of that cosmos – the mineral and animal parts – can be liberated from their temporal existence and attain states of perfection, gold in the case of minerals, and for*

humans, longevity, immortality, and finally redemption. Such transformations can be brought about on the one hand, by the use of a material substance such as 'the philosopher's stone' or elixir, or, on the other hand, by revelatory knowledge or psychological enlightenment.

(H. J. Sheppard, Ambix, *1970, vol. 17, pp. 69–84)*

As William H. Brock points out in his splendid book *The Fontana History of Chemistry*, it is important to recognize not only the two complementary aspects of alchemical activity, the material and the spiritual, but also that time was an important element in alchemy: both material and spiritual perfection take time to achieve, and one of the goals of the alchemist was to speed up what were regarded as natural processes. But for the alchemist:

> *...the attainment of the goals of material, and/or spiritual, perfection will mean a release from time itself: materially through riches and the attainment of independence from worldly economic cares, and spiritually by the achievement of immortality.*
>
> *(W. H. Brock,* The Fontana History of Chemistry, *Fontana Press, 1992, p. 4)*

The search for this unreachable goal did involve a great deal of experimentation, and many significant discoveries were made along the way as well as the development of many of the fundamental chemical techniques. But because of the mystical and occult framework of these experiments very little progress was made in understanding or predicting the properties of matter.

Figure 3.9
The Alchemist by Johannes Stradanus.

Modern chemistry did not begin until the philosophical ideas behind alchemy were essentially abandoned and the scientific method was applied to investigating the constitution and transformations of matter. However, as William H. Brock describes, chemistry presented the early natural philosopher with peculiarly difficult problems:

> *The sheer complexity of most of the chemical materials with which chemists commonly worked can be seen, with hindsight, to have inevitably made generalizations extremely difficult. Chemists were considering with equal ardour the chemical components of the human and animal body, and of plants and minerals, the procedures of metallurgy, pottery, vinegar, acid and glass manufacture, as well as, in some quarters, abstractions like the philosopher's stone and the elixir of life. There was no universally agreed chemical language, no convenient compartmentalization of substances into organic and inorganic, into solids, liquids and gases, or into acids, bases and salts; and no concept of purity. ...*

But perhaps the greatest stumbling block to the further development of chemistry was a case of insufficient analysis – there was a complete absence of a knowledge or concept of the gaseous state of matter. Chemistry remained a two-dimensional science, which studied, and only had equipment and apparatus to handle, solids and liquids.

(W. H. Brock, The Fontana History of Chemistry, *Fontana Press, 1992, p. 42*)

As far as the beginnings of modern chemistry are concerned, many people were responsible for the change to an empirical approach but one of the more important was Robert Boyle (Section 2.2). Pupils in schools used to be taught that Boyle was 'the father of chemistry and the son of the Earl of Cork'. Boyle was called, in his own time, the 'ornament of English science'. He believed that chemistry was the ideal experimental science and he strongly rejected Aristotle's ideas; in fact he rejected Aristotle's entire philosophical framework. Boyle was firm in his opposition to any irrational explanations for natural phenomena, based only on belief.

Aristotle had believed in what are called 'final causes'. This means that everything happens for a reason to do with some future event. This contrasts with what we call the 'mechanistic explanation', which asks what earlier circumstances caused a thing to happen. One major consequence of overthrowing Aristotle's theories about final causes was that it allowed scientists to concentrate on *how* chemical substances behave, rather than *why* they behave as they do. Boyle and others therefore established experimentation as the basis for scientific knowledge.

On the basis of experiments, Boyle argued strongly against the existence of the Greek 'elements' as the building blocks of matter in a famous treatise called *The Sceptical Chymist* (Figure 3.10). Instead, he proposed a new definition of a chemical element, one closer to the modern view and which was capable of experimental investigation:

I now mean by Elements ... certain Primitive and simple ... bodies; which not being made of any other bodies, or of one another, are the Ingredients of which all those call'd perfectly mixt Bodies are immediately compounded and into which they are ultimately resolved.

(R. Boyle, The Sceptical Chymist, *London, 1661*).

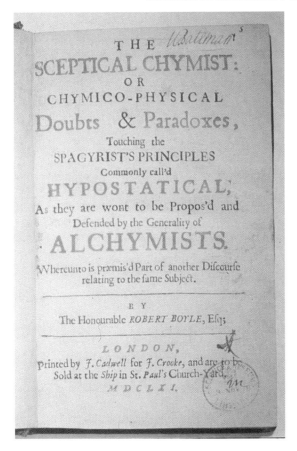

Figure 3.10
Boyle's *The Sceptical Chymist*.

Boyle also started the process of **classification** of chemical substances, by devising series of chemical tests that helped to place substances into particular classes. Classification is a vital part of scientific method, and particularly of chemistry. The gathering together of materials with common properties into classes can help us to make generalizations about chemical structure and reactivity. There are far too many chemicals known (more than 12 million had been characterized by 1993) for us to study the behaviour of every one individually. A class can be large or small. Things can belong to several classes. Sugar is a white solid (one class), it's a food (another), it burns (another), and so on.

Despite these considerable advances, Boyle was, as pointed out earlier, handicapped by the two-dimensionality of a science that did not recognize the importance of the gaseous state of matter.

The crucial chemical role of gases was established in the late 18th century by the genius of the French chemist, Antoine-Laurent Lavoisier (Figure 3.11). The son of a lawyer, he was himself trained as a lawyer. He attended the Collège Mazarin, which was renowned not only for its classical teaching but for science as well. This, combined with his natural inclinations, meant that Lavoisier devoted all his spare time to scientific pursuits. The turning point came when, at the suggestion of a geologist family friend, Jean-Étienne Guettard, he attended a popular chemistry course in 1762, a year before graduating with a baccalaureate in law. In 1763, when Guettard received approval to begin a geological survey of the whole of France, he took Lavoisier with him.

[handwritten margin note: bachelor degree]

In their travels, Lavoisier paid particular attention to water supplies, and it was his later meticulous experiments on the composition and properties of water that led, in 1773, to his realization that there were not just two but three states of matter:

> *All bodies in nature present themselves to us in three different states. Some are solid like stones, earth, salts and metals. Others are fluid like water, mercury, spirits of wine; and others finally are in a third state which I shall call the state of expansion or of vapours, such as water when one heats it above the boiling point.*
>
> *(Quoted in W. H. Brock,* The Fontana History of Chemistry, *Fontana Press, 1992, p. 98)*

Lavoisier's studies led to the publication of his *Traité élémentaire de chimie* (*An Elementary Treatise on Chemistry*) in 1789. In it he defined an element as any substance that could not be broken down further by chemical means, essentially the modern definition. The supremacy of the empirical approach to chemistry is apparent from the fact that a good third of the treatise was devoted to chemical apparatus. Lavoisier was the first to discover that water is composed of hydrogen and oxygen and therefore cannot be an elementary substance. He also reformed the language of chemistry.

Tragically, Lavoisier's life was cut short by the French Revolution. He was hated both as a member of the aristocracy and as a 'tax farmer' [tax collector] and condemned for corresponding with 'the political enemies of France' abroad. Despite the fact that the content of his letters was scientific, he was

Figure 3.11
Antoine-Laurent Lavoisier (1743–1794). One of the founders of modern chemistry, Lavoisier is particularly noted for his discovery of the role of oxygen in chemical reactions. He showed that the process of combustion involves reaction with oxygen in the air, and that oxygen also plays a fundamental role in respiration.

sent to the guillotine on 8 May 1794. The mathematician Lagrange commented 'It required only a moment to sever his head, and probably one hundred years will not suffice to produce another like it.'

For many people today, chemistry seems much less accessible than the other sciences, yet it is arguably *the* central science (Figure 3.12). Studies of the chemistry of compounds of the element carbon, the subject known as **organic chemistry**, overlaps with biochemistry and molecular biology. Much of **inorganic chemistry** (essentially the chemistry of the elements other than carbon) is relevant to geochemistry. Connecting these two areas is the subject of **analytical chemistry**, which deals with the techniques and methods used to analyse substances. The study of the physical properties of different substances and how they react together is the domain of **physical chemistry**, sharing boundaries with physics and materials science, the latter (concerned with the technological properties of different materials) despite its name being a branch of technology! And **theoretical chemistry** becomes in some of its topic areas indistinguishable from applied mathematics.

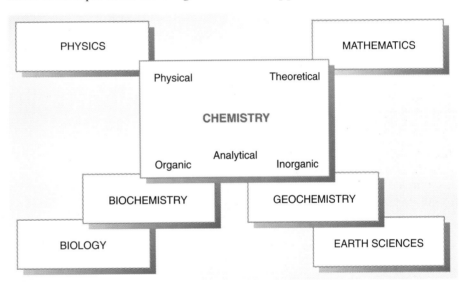

Figure 3.12
Chemistry, the central science.

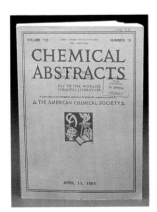

Figure 3.13
An issue of the periodical *Chemical Abstracts*.

Another measure of the breadth and importance of chemistry is the number of publications dealing with chemically related topics. Every publication, be it a book, an article in a scientific journal or a patent document, is indexed and a summary printed in a publication called *Chemical Abstracts* (Figure 3.13), which is published by the American Chemical Society (an abstract means a summary). In 1907, its first year of operation, it published just 12 000 abstracts; in 1992, the number had grown to nearly 530 000 and the cumulative total of abstracts had reached over 14 million. And by the end of 1993, over 12 million different chemical compounds were listed by the *Chemical Abstracts Register*, of which 700 000 were added in 1993 alone. (Notice how large numbers are printed here: groups of three digits are separated by a space, not by a comma or a full stop.)

The growth in the number of abstracts published is illustrated in Figure 3.14. It took thirty years to publish the first million abstracts. Now, more than a million new ones are added every two years. Over 1.5 million documents are surveyed by *Chemical Abstracts* each year, including 10 000 journals. Every five years a new index is prepared of all the material published during that period. At the time of writing, the most recent was the *Twelfth Collective Index*, published in 1992, and covering the period 1987–91. In hardcopy format it consists of 215 880 pages in 115 volumes, and refers to 3 052 700 separate publications dealing with some aspect of chemistry. It occupies 6.7 metres (22 feet) of shelf space and weighs 247 kilograms (544 pounds). It has been submitted to the *Guinness Book of World Records* as the longest index in the world. Given that this is just the index to the summaries of all these publications, imagine how much space all the original documents would occupy. Fortunately, information technology is increasingly being used to assist scientists in their work, and the *Twelfth Collective Index* is also available on just four CD-ROM disks (Figure 3.15).

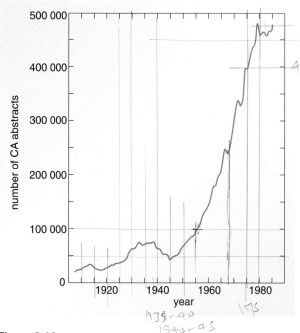

Figure 3.14
The growth of documents included in *Chemical Abstracts* since 1907.

Figure 3.15
Chemical Abstracts Twelfth Collective Index: 115 volumes or four CD-ROM disks.

Summary of Chapter 3

With the vast increase in scientific knowledge, specialization within a particular branch has occurred. In addition to its own knowledge base, each discipline and sub-discipline also has its own techniques and philosophy.

The earliest scientific studies would probably be regarded today as being part of physics. Physics deals with the study of matter and energy from the very large to the very small and includes subjects such as: electricity and magnetism; heat, light and sound; and the forces between objects, including gravity, and their consequent motion.

The first person to apply the modern scientific method to physics was Galileo Galilei working in Italy. He made the crucial distinction between asking *how* did an object fall as opposed to *why* did an object fall, the latter being a matter for philosophy rather than scientific investigation.

Isaac Newton, working in England, made a series of epoch-making discoveries, many of which are still relevant: the Law of Gravitation, the properties of light and its interaction with matter, his three Laws of Motion, and the mathematical technique of calculus were all discovered by him.

Biology is concerned with all living things. Formulating a definition of life is not easy; perhaps the simplest satisfactory definition is that only a living organism is able to reproduce itself.

Andreas Vesalius was the first to advocate the use of dissection on corpses to study human anatomy. William Harvey discovered the circulation of the blood in humans, and showed that the heart is essentially a pump. And Antony van Leeuwenhoek first made use of the microscope to examine microorganisms.

The huge number of species on Earth and the many different levels of study that are possible mean that biology includes a huge number of subject areas. A more appropriate term to embrace such a variety is biological sciences.

There is a lot of research activity at the boundaries of biological sciences with other disciplines, especially in the area known as molecular biology. With the epoch-making discovery of the double helix structure of DNA by James Watson and Francis Crick in 1953 and the consequent deciphering of the genetic code, there has been an explosive growth of knowledge in this area.

Geology is concerned with the Earth's physical environment, its origins and evolution. One of the founding figures of modern geology was Abraham Gottlob Werner, who introduced the idea that rock layers could be produced by the laying down of rock particles produced from pre-existing rock formations. James Hutton put forward the view known as Uniformitarianism. This states that geological activity is constantly occurring and that the processes that took place earlier in the Earth's history could be inferred from the processes occurring now. In other words, 'the present is the key to the past'.

As with biology, the boundaries of geology have expanded in recent years and now include the subjects of geochemistry, geophysics, atmospheric sciences and oceanography. With that expansion has come a new name, Earth sciences, as a more appropriate description of the subject.

Chemistry deals with the composition and transformation of materials. Much early chemistry was concerned with alchemy, the belief that the material parts of the cosmos can attain a state of perfection, gold in the case of minerals. As with the other major scientific disciplines, modern chemistry did not begin until the scientific method was adopted.

Chemistry presented particularly difficult problems to the early natural philosophers. These included (i) the range and complexity of the materials studied; (ii) the absence of an agreed chemical language; (iii) the lack of an appreciation of the concept of purity; and (iv) lack of understanding of the chemical importance of gases.

Two of the most important scientists responsible for the application of the scientific method to chemistry were Robert Boyle and Antoine-Laurent Lavoisier. Boyle was instrumental in applying the empirical approach to chemistry. He started the process of the classification of chemical substances

based on observation or experiment - not theory.

and proposed a new definition of an element. However, he was handicapped by the lack of knowledge of the gaseous state of matter. It was Lavoisier who established the crucial chemical role of gases. He also gave us the modern definition of an element.

Modern chemistry can be divided into a number of (overlapping) areas: organic chemistry, the chemistry of carbon compounds; inorganic chemistry, the chemistry of the other elements; analytical chemistry, the analysis of substances; physical chemistry, the study of the physical properties of substances and their reactions; and theoretical chemistry, the application of mathematical models to chemical problems. Chemistry is arguably the central science, sharing boundaries as it does with biology (through biochemistry), geology (through geochemistry), physics and mathematics.

Another measure of the breadth and importance of chemistry is the number of publications dealing with chemically related topics. The journal *Chemical Abstracts* publishes over half a million abstracts each year. By the end of 1993, nearly 12 million different chemical compounds were listed by the *Chemical Abstracts* Register, of which 700 000 were added in 1993 alone.

Question 8   Classify the following topics according to the scientific discipline(s) or sub-discipline(s) you think are most relevant.

(a) The search for improved devices for the direct conversion of solar energy into electricity.   *Physics – electricity*

(b) The investigation of the toxic properties of the products and by-product materials of a factory making organophosphorus pesticides.   *Organic*

(c) Studies to investigate the possibility of the production of fuels or energy from coal *in situ* (that is, not mining the coal first).   *ORGANIC*

(d) Investigation of the factors affecting the magnitude and time of appearance of the Antarctic ozone hole.

(e) The production of new vaccines by genetic engineering techniques.

Question 9   Give a brief explanation of why the alchemists' aim of turning base metals into gold was reasonable in the light of the theory that matter is composed of the four elements air, earth, fire and water.

Question 10 The graph in Figure 3.14 shows the growth of documents in *Chemical Abstracts* between 1907 and 1985.

(a) When did the number of documents abstracted per year first reach 100 000?   *1946 1955*

(b) How many documents were abstracted in 1975?

(c) In what periods has the number of documents abstracted per year declined year on year?   *> 400,000*   *1914–18*   *1935 – 45*   *1979 – 80*

If you're unsure about how to interpret graphs like this one, you can skip this question for now. Graphs are explained in Section 8.8 and in AV sequence 1.

Chapter 4
Chemistry in action

4.1 Chemistry in context

In the previous Chapter, you saw how wide-ranging a subject chemistry is and how many articles are published each year concerned with chemistry and chemistry-related topics. But these statistics do not reveal in any detail what it is about these topics that makes them chemical. In this Chapter we shall look at some reports of scientific topics that have appeared in newspapers and magazines, and use them to see what questions concerning their chemical aspects they raise in your mind. Each of the five articles relate to one of the five major topic areas in the Course: nutrition, health, energy, materials and the quality of life.

Let's start by trying to put chemistry into context. How many things around you do you think might be made from material that was invented in the 20th century?

Such a list could be very long. Unless you are lying naked on a lonely desert island beach it is probable that you are close to numerous items that are made of modern, synthesized materials. If you wear spectacles with plastic lenses, or contact lenses, then you look at the world through a designed, synthetic material. The coloured dyes used in this book were designed by chemists in laboratories. It is more than likely that some of your clothes are made of acrylic, rayon or nylon. Your watch may have a liquid crystal display. If you have any medicine to hand, that will most likely have been made or designed by chemists. Even the materials that you think of as 'natural', such as wool, wood and cotton, will almost certainly have been treated with something to make their processing easier, or to enhance their looks or wearing properties. When you are struggling with a part of the Course that you may find difficult, remember that chemistry *is* relevant to you and your everyday life, as well as having wider importance. You simply can't avoid chemistry, it's everywhere! (Even your desert island beach is made of chemicals.)

The 20th century revolution in the understanding of chemical processes has radically changed the face of the world. In Britain, the chemical industry is of major economic importance and possibly the biggest of all types of industry. Much of the synthesis of new drugs, plastics, electronic materials, structural materials, perfumes and so on, is based on an understanding and manipulation of the principles that govern chemical change. As well as giving us greater power over our environment, the study of chemistry has had a powerful cultural impact in revealing some of the essential beauty and order of the natural world.

As you read each of the following articles, try to identify those aspects that are specifically chemical, and try to jot down in your notebook any questions that the article raises in your mind. Then read the commentary given after the article to compare with your own ideas. If they do not match completely (they are unlikely to), or even to any great extent, don't be too concerned. Your own thoughts may well be relevant; it is just that in giving our comments, we have the advantage of knowing what is in the rest of the Course!

4.2 When is a chemical not a chemical?

The article in Activity 3 appeared in *The Independent* on 11 February 1993.
It is by David Nicholson-Lord, the paper's consumer affairs correspondent.

Activity 3 Failure to act on toxic apple juice attacked

Consumer groups yesterday attacked the Ministry of Agriculture for failing to make public test results which showed high levels of a toxic chemical in apple juice that was on sale.

Patulin, a naturally-occurring toxin produced by mould, has caused cancers, tumours and liver damage in rats. It is said to be between 57 and 400 times more toxic than the pesticide Alar, the subject of another recent food scare involving apples.

Five out of 32 samples tested for the ministry last March showed levels above the World Health Organisation standard of 50 parts per billion. One was more than eight times higher.

However, the details were only released when John Gummer, the Minister of Agriculture, met consumer groups informally last week. His disclosure was apparently prompted by newspaper inquiries.

The ministry's stance was yesterday condemned by John Beishon, director of the Consumers' Association, as a "blatant disregard for the consumer's right to know which makes a mockery of the Prime Minister's commitment to open government". The public should have been told as soon as the raised levels of patulin were discovered, he said.

His criticisms were echoed by the National Consumer Council and Parents for Safe Food, whose director, Tim Lang, criticised the "institutional collusion" between the ministry and the food industry. Critics called for an independent food safety agency to protect consumers' interests.

The fruit juice industry was told of the findings last July and agreed to tighten up its testing procedures for patulin and bring levels down as low as "technologically possible". The ministry refuses to name the companies whose products breached the WHO limits.

A spokeswoman said medical experts had advised that there was no danger to the public. "Are the critics saying that every time a level is found above a certain guideline we should immediately rush into print with all the details of it?"

In the Commons, the Government faced an emergency question from Labour, which accused it of a "shameless cover-up" and said the information should have been made public and toxic juice taken off shelves.

Nicholas Soames, the food minister, accused Labour of "ridiculous and idiotic scaremongering".

The British Soft Drinks Association has been advised that a person weighing 70 kg (11 stones) would have to drink 10 litres of juice containing more than 50 parts per billion of patulin a week "for a period of time" before there was damage to health. For children, smaller amounts would carry a risk.

About 100 million litres of apple juice are sold each year in the U.K. – less than two litres per person.

The decision not to alert the public last summer was taken on advice from the Department of Health's toxicity committee and with the backing of the Food Advisory Committee, which includes consumer representatives.

Jill Moore, a member of the advisory committee and chairman of the National Consumer Council's food safety policy committee, said patulin had been detected by routine food surveillance but "at the time it didn't seem a very big problem". On the basis of advice from the toxicity committee, she was "quite confident that we were acting sensibly and responsibly".

Mrs Moore added: "I agree absolutely with openness but I think the ministry is right to balance the risk of panic and people stopping buying apple juice. However, with hindsight it was probably wrong not to disclose it last year. When it gets out in this way it causes a much bigger impact. If it had been published last summer it would probably have been a small item in the news in brief."

The controversy has reopened the issue of whether the ministry can represent both consumers and food producers. Critics have long accused it of an 'incestuous' relationship with industry.

Casual reading of this article might have given the impression that once again here was an example of food being contaminated by some product of the chemical industry. Indeed, the pesticide Alar is mentioned, which had earlier been the subject of a scare concerning the toxicity of apples. But more careful study reveals that the toxin, patulin, is naturally occurring and not manufactured, and that the pesticide is much less toxic by comparison. Referring to patulin as 'a toxic chemical', however, tends to reinforce the initial impression.

In recent years, a number of companies have promoted products that are said to be healthier for you by saying that they are made from 'natural materials' or 'organic products'. The producers make claims such as their particular product contains 'no chemicals' or they 'don't use chemicals in their production'. Is it true to say that something does not contain any chemicals? What are chemicals? Is there any difference between naturally occurring substances and manufactured or synthetic ones? Are the former always good and the latter always bad? By the end of the Course we hope that you will be able to answer questions such as these.

▦   You should be able to decide already whether the statement 'are naturally occurring substances always good and manufactured or synthetic ones always bad' is true or false. What information provides an answer?

▦   The fact that patulin is a naturally occurring toxin and not manufactured indicates that the above statement is not true.

As the Course proceeds, you will come across many other examples that serve to show the above generalization to be false. In particular, you will learn more about the chemical composition of foodstuffs in Book 3.

4.3 New drugs for old

The next article for you to consider is in Activity 4 (overleaf). It is a shortened version of the original, which was written by Patricia Mowbray and published in *The Sunday Times Magazine* on 26 July 1992. Read it now.

This article gives a graphic description of one of the main strategies used by pharmaceutical companies to discover new drugs. This is the isolation from a variety of biological sources, often plants, of substances that, when tested, have desirable activity against one or more medical conditions. Another, much more recent, approach is to design the drug from scratch using computer-modelling and other techniques, and you will learn more about this method in Book 4. But as with the earlier article, it raises a number of questions that need to be answered to appreciate fully what is involved in drug discovery. Some questions are:

●   How are substances extracted from plant material such as yew bark or clippings from yew trees?

●   What is meant by partial synthesis, semi-synthesis and total synthesis of a substance such as taxol?

●   How do taxol, taxotere and taxinine differ in their chemical make-up?

[handwritten annotation: artificial production of compounds from their constituents]

Activity 4 Cancer: a new way out

Every decade sees a new drug emerge which has a significant impact on the treatment of cancer and raises hopes in the families of patients with advanced tumours. Taxol, possibly destined to become the cancer drug of the Nineties, has taken America by storm and put cancer centres under siege from patients begging for this scarce new drug, extracted from the bark of yew trees in the ancient forests of the Pacific Northwest.

Taxol has excited researchers and physicians, because it works in a different way to their existing anti-cancer arsenal and could prove a new weapon against tumours resistant to other treatments. It has excited the American press even more, for here was a gem of a story – a media 'miracle drug' which created an environmental dilemma.

To produce enough taxol to provide one course of treatment for one cancer patient means destroying three 100-year-old Pacific yew trees. With a finite number of trees available it was clear that, while current stands of this slow-growing yew could provide enough taxol for experimental trials, they would not provide enough to treat an entire cancer patient population.

The taxol story has taken 30 years to hit the headlines. In 1962 a botanist involved in a National Cancer Institute (NCI) natural products programme collected samples of the Pacific yew in an Oregon forest. By the mid-Sixties chemists had isolated the active molecule of the sample and called it taxol.

"The Americans hardly pursued this with enthusiasm," says Professor Gordon McVie, scientific director of the U.K.'s Cancer Research Campaign, which is funding several clinicians running British trials of taxol and a similar drug, taxotere. "This phenomenal drug simply got buried. They sat on it for 20 years. Now they have come under pressure from patient lobby groups and environmentalists and are racing to make up for lost time."

In the U.S.A. taxol is currently in phase three trials for the treatment of ovarian cancer at the NCI and phase two trials for the treatment of other tumours such as breast, lung, head and neck. Phase two studies involve testing a drug to determine its safety and efficacy. Once this is demonstrated it moves into phase three, involving more patients and enabling a more accurate picture to be obtained of safety and results.

After the encouraging results from clinical trials NCI, which had been responsible for co-ordinating the collection of yew bark and the manufacture of taxol, realised that it needed help from the private sector to obtain enough taxol for further trials and to get the drug approved and marketed quickly. In January 1991 NCI made a deal with the American drug company Bristol-Myers Squibb. In exchange for exclusive access to the NCI clinical data, needed to support marketing approval, the company agreed to supply taxol free to NCI for clinical research and to prepare and submit a new drug application. It also agreed to investigate alternative sources of taxol.

At present yew bark is the only source of taxol used for cancer patients, but Bristol-Myers Squibb says that it recognises that the Pacific yew tree is a finite resource, and not a viable source for long-term production of the drug.

It has entered into a dozen agreements with various companies, researchers and universities to develop other sources. These include extracting taxol from twigs and needles of various yew species without destroying trees, and semi-synthesis to convert natural material into taxol. Florida State University researchers have patented one such process.

Meanwhile, in France, scientists discovered a technique for partial synthesis of a compound obtained by using the needles of the European yew or *Taxus baccata,* a tree often seen in English churchyards and traditionally a symbol both of grief because of its drooping needles and of resurrection because of its longevity. Rhone-Poulenc Rorer, the French pharmaceutical company, under an agreement with the Institut Chimie des Substances Naturelles, is developing the drug taxotere using this method.

Patented in 1986, taxotere has a slightly different chemical structure to taxol and several advantages. Apart from its renewable source of yew needles, it has better water solubility and may be easier to administer. Taxol has to be infused in Cremaphor before being administered, a solvent which has been associated with allergic and hypersensitive reactions.

Two British chemists, Dr Paul Jenkins from Leicester University and Dr Nicholas Lawrence from UMIST, are also working on a synthetic version of taxol and have an agreement to take an annual 2000 kilos of yew clippings from the maze at Longleat, Wiltshire, for their research.

Dr Jenkins says that he hopes this year to

produce a synthetic form of taxinine, a compound isolated from European yew clippings, and within five years a total synthesis of taxol. He also hopes "to discover other important taxol-mimicking compounds along the way".

Both the Cancer Research Campaign and the Imperial Cancer Research Fund are helping to fund trials of the new drugs, which are now taking place in the U.K.

The Royal Marsden in London was the first hospital in this country to use taxol for patients with ovarian cancer. Trials began about a year ago. In May it became the first centre in the U.K. to start trials of taxol for patients with breast cancer. Dr Ian Smith, consultant cancer physician, says that further trials involving cancer of the colon and lung are in the planning stages.

The real encouragement to physicians is that taxol works in a different way to other treatment which patients may have become resistant to.

"During cancer growth, cells divide and proliferate," says Dr Smith. "Cell division requires the formation of an internal skeleton called microtubules. Taxol interferes with microtubule function so that the cells cannot divide and the cancer cannot grow.

At Edinburgh's medical oncology unit of the Western General Hospital, Professor John Smyth's team began trials of taxotere in May. "In laboratory tests taxotere appears to be more potent than taxol but that does not mean that it will be a better drug," he says. "However, because you need less of it you can treat more people."

"This is not some miracle drug which is going to cure cancer," says Professor Smyth. "But taxol and taxotere are exciting compounds to those of us who spend so much time losing in this difficult field. We try a lot of things which don't succeed and there is evidence that these drugs are going to help some patients.

Professor Gordon McVie of the Cancer Research Campaign says that "here we have an exciting new compound which has at last become a high priority for everyone. We are likely to see both taxol and taxotere accepted. The fact that there are two of them and that they are already competing is good news. It will stop price fixing and benefit the health service and the patients in the end."

- What is the mode of action of these substances in treating cancer?
- Why are the British chemists likely to discover other 'taxol-mimicking compounds' in their search for a synthetic version of taxol?

Answers to some of these questions require a substantial input from biology, but the relationship between chemical make-up of a drug and its activity is the concern of the group of scientists known as medicinal chemists, and they use the techniques and methods of chemistry in their work. You will learn more about drugs and their role in combating disease in Book 3.

4.4 Fuels paradise

Activity 5 (overleaf) shows an article by Christian Wolmar, transport correspondent of *The Independent*. It appeared on 3 November, 1992. Read it now.

This article raises some interesting questions in discussing the use of rape seed oil as an alternative to diesel.

- What questions come to your mind that are raised by the article but not answered?
- Some possible ones are: What is diesel fuel made of? How does this compare with rape seed oil? Are there other plants that produce suitable fuels for use in vehicles? What is involved in obtaining oil from rape seed? Why does diesel generate sulfur dioxide giving rise to acid rain whereas rape seed oil does not?

Activity 5   Buses to use rape seed fuel for trial period

Three buses in Reading will today become Britain's first to run on rape seed oil instead of diesel. They will use a fuel called 'Diesel-Bi', produced by Novamont, an Italian company, for the next three months as an experiment.

The fuel is more expensive to use than diesel, and Reading Buses is calling on the Government to create a favourable tax regime because of its environmental benefits.

The manufacturers say the oil, which has been refined from rape seed oil, harms the environment much less than conventional fuels. It generates no sulphur dioxide, one of the principal components of acid rain, and emission levels of black particles and smoke are lower. It is biodegradable, so spillages cause little damage.

The fuel could also help the Government to meet targets for reducing levels of carbon dioxide emission; during the growth period of the rape seed the gas is absorbed from the atmosphere, so the net emission is zero.

The oil can be used in diesel engines without any modification. There are already a number of similar experiments in Italy, France, Austria and Germany. The producer, anxious to establish an experiment in Britain, approached Reading Buses, which will use the fuel on three different types of bus for three months to assess the effect on performance.

Paul Shepherd, Reading Buses' engineering director, said that with favourable trial results and government support the fuel could be economically viable.

He said that the pump price of the rape seed oil, which was not taxed, was comparable with that of diesel which was taxed. The company, however, obtained a rebate for the duty paid on diesel and therefore the rape seed oil was costing it "two or three times more per gallon".

According to Customs and Excise, EC regulations will mean that from 1 January 1993, the same rate will be imposed on diesel substitutes as on diesel. Mr Shepherd said his company would be campaigning against this change.

During the Course, we shall be examining different fuels, both in Book 2 in the context of energy and in Book 4 as we consider the potential for renewable energy sources. One of the issues that you may well be aware of relates to the use of fossil fuels, a finite and non-renewable source, compared with renewable fuels. The former adds to the atmospheric burden of carbon dioxide, and hence adds to the natural greenhouse effect, whereas the latter has no net effect. The problem is that present oil and natural gas prices encourage the use of fossil fuels rather than renewable fuels such as rape seed oil, as the article alludes to. A report giving the results of the trial was published in November 1993. It identified cost as the major hindrance to a large-scale use of rape seed oil as a fuel. There were minor technical differences, some of which favoured Diesel-Bi over diesel. However, it was anticipated that with further trials, these technical issues could be resolved. The cost issue, depending as it does on taxation policy and the economies of scale, requires political and social judgements, as well as economic ones, to be made. We shall address some of these wider issues from time to time, as well as providing information about some of the more scientific and technical questions listed above.

4.5 A material world

Now consider the item in Activity 6. Written by Robert Matthews, it is based on an article in the scientific journal *Nature* (volume 326, p. 580), and was published in *The Times* on 1 May 1987. Read it now.

This article deals with what are now more usually called synthetic fibres, the [made by synthesis – joining up parts] discovery of which dates back to the 1930s. Since that time they have played an increasingly important role in the lives of developed countries, and they are used for a wide range of purposes from clothing to cars and from climbing

Compound whose molecule is formed from large number repeated units

---

Activity 6 Taking the heat out of man-made fibres

One property of natural fibres, such as wool, that textile scientists have long tried to mimic is the way in which their constituent polymers naturally bind up into usable fibres.

Man-made fibres have to be made by polymerising the base material, melting or dissolving the product, and either squirting or extruding it into strands.

But now a South Korean polymer scientist, Dr Han Sik Yoon, of the Fibre and Polymer Synthesis Laboratory in Seoul, claims to have found a material that turns itself into fibres without the need for heat.

By eliminating an energy intensive process, the development opens up the possibility of lower production costs, and cheaper clothing.

The molecules of many man-made materials, such as nylon, are very flexible, with only weak forces between the polymer chains, which tend to tangle up randomly. To get the chains to form strong fibres, these chains have to be warmed and drawn out.

Nature achieves this automatically in materials like wool. What Dr Han Sik Yoon has discovered is the same phenomenon of 'self-assembly' in an aromatic polyamide called poly-*p*-phenylene-terephthalamide (PPT-A), a close relative of Kevlar, and the fire-resistant material Nomex.

The compound is similar to silk in that it consists of stiff polymer chains which interact strongly between each other. The research has shown that the PPT-A becomes a gel when polymerised with dimethylacetamide, which then reacts to form the long, spirally-twisted fibres resembling those of flax. This shape results because the molecular aggregation forces operating over just a few billionths of a metre hold the chains tightly together.

Dr Han Sik Yoon speculates that this crucial chain-packing mechanism found with PPT-A may prove to be a universal one that applies to the formation of all fibrous materials in nature, as PPT-A has certain similarities at a molecular level with nature's cellulose-like fibres.

Polymer chemists will now be searching for ways of making other man-made fibres show the same self-assembling phenomenon.

---

ropes to armour-plating. In some of their uses they have replaced traditional materials and in other cases they are used for completely new applications where there was otherwise no suitable existing material. But what are they? How do they relate to natural fibres?

Although the source for this article was the scientific journal *Nature*, the article itself is a report published in *The Times* newspaper with the purpose of informing the general public about advances in the development of new types of synthetic fibre. Clearly, however, in contrast to the earlier articles, a much greater number of scientific and technical terms have been used and, to someone without some technical background, would probably have made little sense. In attempting to phrase questions that this article raises, it could well be difficult for such a person to know where to start. What is a polymer? What is the process of polymerization and what are the materials needed to make it happen? What do the molecules of synthetic fibres, such as nylon, look like, and how do they compare with those of natural polymers? What are the mysterious forces that operate at the microscopic level of billionths of a metre? What does the long name tell us about the nature of PPT-A? And what do we know about the shapes and properties of different sorts of fibre chains, and how is this knowledge used to design and make new ones?

Book 2 of the Course deals with some of these issues. There you will learn not only about synthetic materials, such as polymers, but also about traditional ones, such as glass, pottery and other ceramics, and a wide variety of metals. It is in the area of materials science that some of the most exciting developments are taking place at the moment, and in Book 4 we shall describe some of the new materials that are currently under investigation.

4.6 The quality of life

The last article for you to look at is shown in Activity 7. It is a shortened version of one that appeared in *The Financial Times* on 12 February 1993, written by Della Bradshaw.

Activity 7 On the scent of a bestsmeller

The dream of every perfumer is not fields of purple lavender nor hillsides covered in bright yellow mimosa – not even gardens full of sweet-smelling roses. It is the one synthetic chemical that will give that most elusive of products – the best-selling fragrance.

For although a perfume may boast high notes of jasmine or undertones of musk, these days the vast majority of perfume oils are produced in a chemistry laboratory rather than a field.

"The trend is towards more synthetic components," points out Terry Goodacre, senior perfumer at Drogoco, one of the dozen fragrance and flavour companies now employed by the top perfume houses to develop new perfumes. He acknowledges that naturally-derived oils "always have the edge", because each fragrance oil can be made up of thousands of individual chemical components, each in minute proportions.

But recent developments in synthesizing oils that replicate natural flower fragrances, and the development of completely new chemical components, are beginning to rival – and even outperform – their natural counterparts.

One big advantage of synthetic oils is that they are less expensive than their natural equivalents. Grasse in the south of France, for example, provided many of the flowers for the perfume industry until tourism pushed up the price of land along the French coast and made large-scale flower cultivation uneconomical. It takes a tonne of jasmine flowers to produce just a few kilos of perfume oil.

The price, quality and supply of synthetics can also be guaranteed. When frost hit the Californian orange crop in December 1991, for example, the price of natural orange oil soared. And until recently, perfumers have imported much of their oak moss and lavender from the former Yugoslavia and many of the resinous fragrances from Somalia. There are now fears that supplies from both these areas could be jeopardised.

The art of the chemist is twofold. First, scientists have to formulate a chemical oil that is as near as possible to the natural source. Traditionally, that has been done by extracting the oil from the plant and then analysing it. But many of the latest high-priced perfumes have used fragrances derived by a new method known as "head space analysis".

In this, rather than analysing the flower oil, scientists concentrate on the odour which emanates from the living flower before it is picked. This can be particularly useful with flowers such as daffodils, from which oil cannot be extracted.

The volatile substances from the flower are vacuumed up over several hours or days. The sweet-smelling air is cooled to condense out the fragrant materials. These are analysed using traditional spectrometry and, if all goes according to plan, replicated.

The difference between the analysis of a flower oil and the results of the vacuum method can be "quite startling", says Goodacre.

One reason for this is that when oils are extracted from flowers, many of the component chemicals are broken down, affecting the smell.

Analytical techniques used to catalogue the volatile components of a natural oil have now become so sophisticated that they can identify those that appear in minute quantities – just a few parts per million. So chemists can go back to popular flowers – the rose is the obvious case – and synthesize these trace chemicals so that the artificial rose oil smells even more like that from the original flower.

Second, and more excitingly, chemists are discovering new fragrant components. "All the time we're looking for new smells, we're all striving for this new component," says Tony Mills, chief perfumer with Bush Boake Allen, the fragrance and flavour company. "With chemistry, we can come up with a whole new direction."

Few perfumers even dare to believe that they will concoct the second Chanel No 5 – a constant bestseller since it was introduced in 1923. What they hope for is a fragrance which other perfume houses will be forced to emulate.

Failing that, they aspire to create a novel fragrance by experimenting with existing chemicals in innovative mixes. Typically, each perfume is a blend of 30 to 50 different oils, although a complex blend can contain up to 200 components.

"It's very exciting to build a winning fragrance around an ingredient that has been on the shelf all the time," says Mills. On the BBA shelves there are up to 1,300 different chemicals.

In spite of all the research involved in creating the vital combination of oils and aromas, as little as 15 per cent of a bottle of perfume is actually oil, says Peter McDougall, an analyst at BZW, the London securities house. The most plentiful component is alcohol – 55 per cent – followed by distilled water. In a bottle of eau de parfum the oil content can be as low as 8 per cent, and in eau de toilette as low as 4 per cent.

And in terms of the cost of production, the ingredients in a bottle of perfume account for only 5 per cent of the total outlay, adds McDougall. The research and development costs a further 5 per cent and there is the additional cost of the expensive equipment needed for the distillation process.

But for those eager to buy their loved ones a bottle of the latest perfume for Valentine's Day on Sunday, it is sobering to remember that most of its cost is accounted for not by the fragrance but by sales and marketing activities, packaging, distribution, and, of course, the profit margin.

For some people, this article may confirm their worst fears about the activities of chemists in tampering with every aspect of our lives! Surely the time-honoured method of producing something so personal as perfume should not be under threat from a 'synthetic' product. Yet this emotional type of response, though very understandable, is also a little irrational. After all, one of the foundations of the scientific approach is reasoning based on experimental evidence.

One of the first things that this article illustrates is that most natural substances that we come across in our daily routine are mixtures, often very complex mixtures. As a consequence, their properties are very difficult to investigate in terms of the well-established theories of the behaviour of individual chemicals. There are very few everyday substances that a chemist would regard as being pure. One possible one would be distilled water, used for steam irons or topping up car batteries; another might be table salt, although that often has small amounts of another substance added to make it flow more freely. The question is, how do we know if a substance is a mixture? The opposite side of the coin is to ask how chemists assess the purity of a substance.

The article refers to the 'new' method known as head-space analysis. In fact, this technique is not a different method of analysis from that used previously, and it is not even that new. Chemists have available a particularly powerful technique for separating the individual components in a complex mixture of a substance such as a perfume: it is called chromatography. It was developed originally for separating natural coloured pigments, hence the derivation of its name, from the Greek *chromos* meaning colour. There are various types of chromatography, but the one commonly used in the perfumery industry is called gas chromatography because the samples are vaporized before being swept through a tube containing a material that separates the different components. The head-space method just refers to the technique for getting the sample into the tube; the method of analysis is essentially the same as previously used.

The other major question raised by this article relates to the nature of substances: it is the question that came up in a different context from the first article – is there any difference between naturally occurring substances and the same substance produced synthetically? The answer that any chemist would give is a categorical no! The alcohol that is found in a bottle of fine champagne (and which is called ethanol by chemists) is identical with that found in methylated spirits produced industrially. The difference is in the substances that accompany the alcohol: in the champagne, substances that make the drinking a pleasurable (if expensive) experience; in methylated spirits, substances that taste bitter and are poisonous which are added deliberately to deter people from drinking it. The essential ingredient in white vinegar (called ethanoic acid, or commonly acetic acid), which is usually made industrially, is the same as that in the wine vinegar used in gourmet cooking. Yet again, it is the substances that accompany the acetic acid that make all the difference.

In Book 4, you will learn more about perfumes, and about why different substances smell the way that they do. The topics of purity and of chemical identity will be major themes throughout the Course as they lie at the very heart of chemistry.

The time has now come to move on to examine the fundamentals of chemistry, to begin to learn its language, and to find out why chemists for so much of their time have to contemplate the make-up of matter on the sub-microscopic scale. Before we can do that, however, we need briefly to examine what we mean by 'scale'.

Summary of Chapter 4

In the previous Chapter, we saw how wide-ranging a subject chemistry is. But these statistics do not reveal in any detail what it is about these topics that makes them chemical. In this Chapter we examined some reports of scientific topics that have appeared in newspapers and magazines to gain a better idea of the kinds of topics and issues that chemistry is concerned with.

It is difficult to avoid contact with some aspect of chemistry. Many of the materials we take for granted are 20th century products. Synthetic fibres, plastics, liquid crystals and modern dyes are just a few of the materials that have been designed and/or made by chemists. The 20th century revolution in the understanding of chemical processes has radically changed the face of the world. As well as giving us greater power over our environment, the study of chemistry has had a powerful cultural impact in revealing some of the essential beauty and order of the natural world.

Five articles were presented, which raised a number of important questions about our chemical environment and about how the public perception of the influence of chemistry contrasts with that of chemists themselves. Examples are: What is a chemical? Is there any difference between naturally occurring substances and manufactured or synthetic ones? Are the former always good and the latter always bad?

Other questions are: How are new drugs discovered? If substances that are used as drugs occur naturally in plants, why are they often also made in a laboratory? How does diesel compare with rape seed oil? Are there other plants that produce oils suitable for use as fuels? What is a polymer? What is a molecule? What do the molecules of synthetic fibres, such as nylon, look like, and how do they compare with those of natural polymers? What are the mysterious forces that operate between molecules? How do we know if a substance is a mixture? And finally, how do chemists assess the purity of a substance?

Question 11 Read the article in Activity 8, which is a shortened version of one that was published in *The Sunday Times* on 24 September 1989; it was written by Jane Bird. Write down in your notebook the questions about the chemical aspects of its content that it raises in your mind. Then compare your questions with the answer given at the back of the book.

Activity 8 'Silver bullet' kills toxic waste

An offshoot of the UK Atomic Energy Authority has devised a cheap, safe method of electrochemical destruction that turns dangerous wastes into carbon dioxide and water.

One man's trash may be another man's treasure, but few people are rushing to collect toxic waste. The public outcry over last month's consignment of PCBs (polychlorinated biphenyls) from Canada suggests that noxious chemicals are now the most unwelcome cargo of all.

But new outlets for poisonous wastes are urgently needed: traditional landfill sites are being withdrawn following the discovery that buried chemicals may eventually leach into the water supply. Third World countries, which previously took the West's waste, are closing their doors, and the practice of burning and dumping at sea is soon to be banned.

Now an alternative solution, dubbed the "silver bullet", has been invented by a British scientist at Dounreay's AEA Technology, the entrepreneurial new arm of the UK Atomic Energy Authority. Dr David Steele, deputy manager of chemical processes, has come up with a cheap, safe method of electrochemical destruction that turns toxic waste into carbon dioxide and water. All that remains is a tiny quantity of residue.

Until now the most acceptable method of dealing with toxic waste has been high-temperature incineration, which oxidises the carbon content of organic materials. Stringent rules governing the operation of commercial incinerators have restricted their number to just three in Britain.

Steele hit on the silver bullet while working on something quite different. He was trying to recover nuclear fuel from pellets whose manufacture had fallen below specification. The problem was that plutonium is highly insoluble and requires particularly aggressive acids to break it down.

"I was trying to help the plutonium on its way by putting it in an electrochemical cell containing silver salt and nitric acid, and passing a current through," says Steele. He found that the silver salt was converted into a form that had a highly oxidising effect, making the plutonium soluble.

Steele had the idea that the silver might also oxidise organic material such as the tissues, brush sweepings and rubber gloves used by scientists in the preparation of nuclear fuel. These items cannot be incinerated because of their radioactive component so they are stored in concrete containers. Some anti-nuclear campaigners have raised the objection that they could eventually biodegrade and cause the radioactivity to migrate through the concrete.

Steele set up a cell with the silver salt and nitric acid and added a tissue. There was an immediate reaction. The solution went from dark brown to colourless and the tissue disappeared. "I added more and more tissues and each one disappeared, leaving the silver solution behind unchanged," he says.

"The penny dropped that here was the beginning of a method that could be used to dispose of contaminated organic material."

The process consumes organic material, oxygen and electricity, to yield carbon dioxide, a small amount of carbon monoxide, water and a tiny amount of residue which can be converted into glass for ultra compact storage.

One of the chief advantages of the silver bullet compared with incineration is that it works at between 55 °C and 95 °C, compared with the 1,100 °C that must be sustained for two seconds in an incinerator in order to destroy PCBs.

And for small quantities it is more economic than incineration. "Whereas the big incineration companies handle between 20,000 and 30,000 tons per year, we could handle one tenth or even one hundredth of that," says Steele.

So far the method has been shown to work with materials which arise in the nuclear industry such as rubber, polyurethane, epoxy resins, lubricating oil and solvents. But Steele says it is also suitable for industrial wastes such as PCBs; pesticide and herbicide residues; phenols produced in the manufacture of laminates; and chlorinated solvents used for industrial cleaning.

Chapter 5
The scale of matter

One effect that the exploration of space has had on the public at large is to emphasize the relative scales of objects within the Universe: the almost unimaginable distances to even the nearest stars; the size of the Solar System and the relative smallness of Earth in comparison; and the finite nature of Earth and its physical resources. Simultaneously, the improvement in our knowledge of the fundamental building blocks of matter itself and the emergence of techniques both for seeing and manipulating matter on a sub-microscopic scale require the ability to appreciate and understand the relative sizes of the very small. Increasingly, it is necessary not just to discuss topics such as these in a descriptive way, but also to be able to use numbers to quantify our discussion. How can objects of such disparate sizes be discussed without the numbers involved becoming unwieldy and awkward? You are about to find out! We begin by looking at the way we measure lengths and distances.

This Chapter deals with the relative sizes of things and the scales used to measure them. It covers scientific notation, the definition and units of length, and the SI system of measurement. If you already have some background in science, you may wish to skim through what follows or even, if you feel sufficiently confident, skip the chapter altogether.

5.1 Lengths and their units

In the United Kingdom, distances are still largely measured in what are known as Imperial units: the mile, and its subdivisions the yard, foot and inch. In this, we are kept company by the United States, which also still uses the mile. However, the awkward relationships of 12 inches to the foot, 3 feet to the yard, and 1 760 yards to the mile, are such that the UK is slowly joining the rest of Europe in adopting the metric system for all measurements. The metric system has been in use for scientific purposes for many years, and so scientists have had to be fluent with both systems; now, the general public are slowly being educated in the use of metric measurements (Figure 5.1), and in due course the Imperial system will doubtless disappear from general use, as have such units as the cubit and league.

Figure 5.1
Educating the motorist!

The **metric system** of length is based on a standard distance called the **metre**. The metre originated in Napoleonic times, and was meant to correspond to one ten-millionth of the distance from the Equator to the North Pole along a meridian passing through Dunkirk and Barcelona, and also near Paris. In practice, the astronomers of the time were unable to measure this distance very accurately, and so in 1889 a more practical standard was created.

This consisted of a bar made from an alloy (mixture) of the two metals platinum and iridium kept at a fixed temperature (the temperature of melting ice). This particular alloy was chosen because of its exceptional hardness and resistance to corrosion. The metre was defined as the distance between two fine lines inscribed on the bar. This standard metre still exists. It is kept at the International Bureau of Weights and Measures at Sèvres, near Paris (Figure 5.2). Copies of this bar (known as secondary standards) were made and distributed to national standards offices throughout the world.

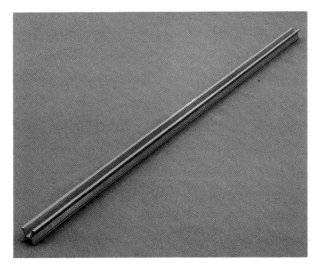

Figure 5.2
The platinum–iridium standard metre.

In more recent times, the platinum–iridium standard metre bar itself became inadequate for many scientific purposes, not to mention the inconvenience of having to make comparisons with a bar kept in a standards laboratory. What was needed was a new method of standardizing the metre, and one that could be readily used in laboratories all over the world.

You will learn later in the Course that light travels as a wave, and that different colours correspond to different wavelengths, that is the distance between one wave and the next (Figure 5.3). Certain atoms give out light of a particular colour, such as the yellow-orange light of certain types of street lamp (Figure 5.4), and this light is often very pure, that is to say it has a very precise wavelength. It is possible to measure this wavelength, and use it as a standard. In 1961, the standard metre was defined as 1 650 763.73 wavelengths of the orange-red light given out by the noble gas krypton (Figure 5.5).

Figure 5.3
The wave nature of light, showing how the wavelength is defined and that red light has a longer wavelength than blue light.

Figure 5.4
Street lamps. The light from this particular type comes
from the element sodium, and is the same as the yellow-
orange flashes sometimes seen during cooking when
water to which salt has been added splashes into the gas
flame.

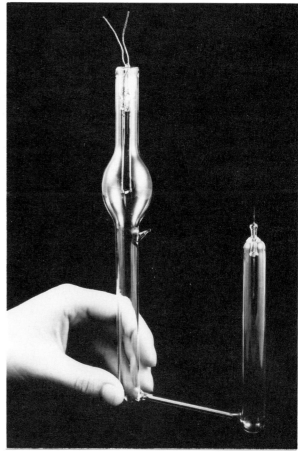

Figure 5.5 (right)
Krypton lamps of the type used to define the metre in the
period 1961 to 1983.

Subsequently, it became apparent that the wavelength of light emitted by
krypton did vary very slightly depending on the circumstances. So in 1983 it
was decided to define the metre in terms of the speed of light in a vacuum. As
a consequence of Einstein's theory of relativity, scientists are convinced that
the speed of light in a vacuum is a constant and the same everywhere. So
now, the metre is defined by the relationship that light travels *exactly*
299 792 458 metres in one second. The rather unwieldy number arises
because scientists wanted to keep the value of the defined metre as close to
the previously measured value as possible.

The metre is a convenient unit for measuring the length of a swimming pool
(25 or 50 metres for Olympic-size pools) or the distance around a running
track (400 metres). But for larger distances, such as the distance between
London and Paris (342 000 metres), or for smaller distances, such as the size
of a piece of A4 paper (0.210 metre by 0.297 metre), a metre is not very
convenient, and so subsidiary units have been devised. You will already be
familiar with the kilometre for larger distances and the millimetre for smaller
distances, but you may not be familiar with their origin.

The metric system for measuring length is part of an all-encompassing
measuring system known as the **SI system** (from the French *Système
International*). We shall express all measurements in the Course using SI
units, but we shall introduce them gradually as we need to make use of them.

Within the SI system, the prefix kilo- is universally used to mean one thousand times larger, and milli- is used to mean one thousand times smaller, or one-thousandth. An additional intermediate prefix that is often used is centi-, which means one hundred times smaller, or one-hundredth. Applying these prefixes to the metre gives the units kilometre, millimetre and centimetre.

For brevity and convenience, instead of using the full name, the unit is often given a symbol: for metre the symbol is m; by extension, the symbols for millimetre, centimetre and kilometre are mm, cm and km, respectively. These units, their sizes and their symbols are summarized in Table 5.1.

Table 5.1 Some SI units of length

Prefix	Size	Symbol
kilometre	1 000 metres	km
metre	standard	m
centimetre	1/100 of a metre	cm
millimetre	1/1 000 of a metre	mm

Box 5.1 Which units of length?

Pamela Anderton, in *A Random Walk in Science*, edited by E. Mendoza (The Institute of Physics, 1973), p. 69.

Units of length have been available to the general public for a long time but the recent drive to advertise one particular brand has led us to publish this report for the assistance of our members.

Brands
We found that the units fell into fairly well defined brands or 'systems' from which we have selected three in general use. Two of these, the 'Rule of Thumb' and the 'British' (known as 'Imperial Standard' in the days when we had an empire) are manufactured in this country; the third, the 'Metric', is imported but fairly readily obtainable.

Tests
We asked a panel of members to use units of the selected brands and to comment on their convenience. We also submitted samples to a well-known laboratory to find out how reliable they were. The selected units and the results of the tests are listed in the table.

Conclusions
The 'Rule of Thumb' was cheap, robust, very convenient and readily obtainable. On the other hand, it was not sufficiently accurate for all purposes.

The 'British' was convenient and readily obtainable, but some doubts exist as to its reliability. Nevertheless, it seems likely to remain popular for a long time.

The 'Metric' is very reliable but not always as convenient to use as the other brands.

Best buys
For general use – Rule of Thumb.

For scientists and for others whose arithmetic is weak – Metric.

Brand	Unit	Reliability	Convenience in use
Metric	'micron'	excellent	fair[a]
British	thou	good	good
Rule of Thumb	hair's breadth	poor	hopeless
Metric	millimetre	excellent	fair[b]
British	inch	good	good
Rule of Thumb	thumb	poor	excellent
Metric	metre	excellent	good
British	yard	fair to good[c]	good
	foot	good	good
Rule of Thumb	pace of stride	fair	excellent
	foot (size of shoe)	fair to good[d]	excellent

[a] Difficult to handle for everyday use and available to special order only.
[b] Our panel found it about 25.4 times too small.
[c] Some samples tended to shrink.
[d] Users with big feet get better results.

5.2 Everyday scales

Most people at some time or another have had to consult a map. It may be to find an unfamiliar address in an adjacent town or to visit some friends or relatives in another region of the country. It may be to undertake a touring holiday abroad. In each case, it is essential to choose an appropriate map, one that shows sufficient detail yet is not so large that the map is totally unwieldy. If the journey is a touring holiday, then maps that show the overall route and local town plans are both required.

▨   How would you define a map?

■   A map is a representation of a selected area of the Earth's surface on a smaller scale.

▨   With this definition of a map, what do you think differentiates the map used for route-planning from a town plan?   ·

■   It is the extent of the reduction. The one is said to be at a different scale to the other.

Typically, a map could have a scale of 1 to 100 000, which is usually written as a ratio, 1 : 100 000.

▨   What does this mean?

■   Each unit of length on the map corresponds to a distance of 100 000 units over the Earth's surface. For example, 1 cm on the map corresponds to 100 000 cm (1 000 m or 1 km) over the Earth's surface.

In choosing a map, then, it is important to suit the scale to the purpose. If the reduction is too great, then the map may not show all the small roads that you need to find your destination. Such a map is said to have too *small* a scale, that is it makes some of the features of interest too small on the map. If the reduction is not sufficient, it may not be possible to include the region between your starting point and your destination on a single map, which is very convenient when planning the overall route. Such a map is said to have too *large* a scale, that is it makes some of the features of interest too large on the map. Indeed, if the scale is very large, the number of maps required to cover the entire journey becomes so large as to be impractical and too expensive.

Figure 5.6a–f shows the effect of different scales on the representation of the area around the headquarters of The Open University at Walton Hall in Milton Keynes.

> **Question 12** The smallest-scale map (1 : 500 000) in Figure 5.6 has 1 mm representing 0.5 km (500 000 mm or 500 m). Work out the ratio for the largest-scale map (1 : 10 000): how many metres does 1 mm represent?.

The maps shown in Figure 5.6 cover a range of scales from 1 : 500 000 to 1 : 10 000, that is a range of 50 times (obtained by dividing 500 000 by 10 000).

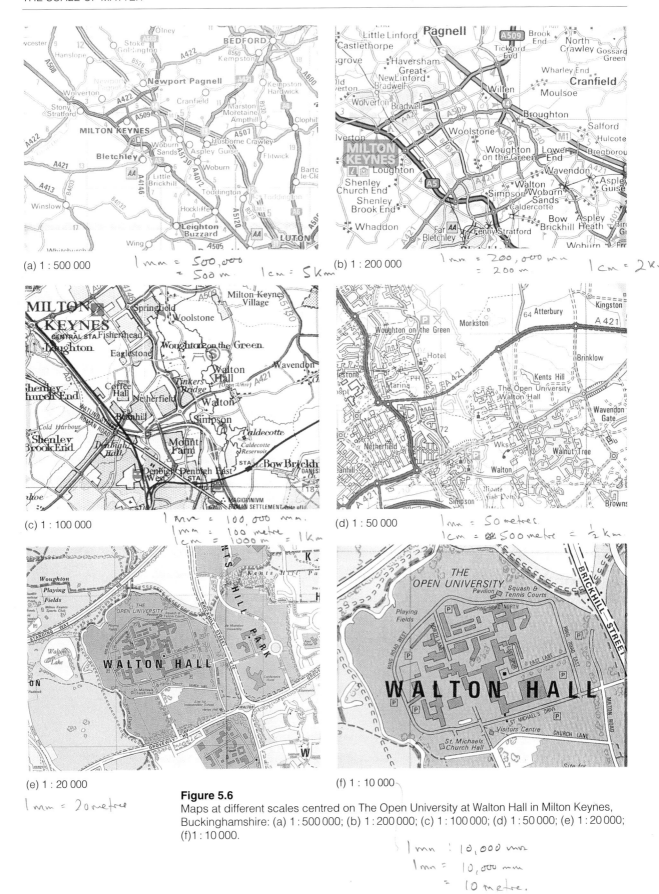

(a) 1 : 500 000

1 mm = 500,000
= 500 m. 1 cm = 5 km

(b) 1 : 200 000

1 mm = 200,000 mm
= 200 m   1 cm = 2 km

(c) 1 : 100 000

1 mm = 100,000 mm.
1 mm = 100 metre
1 cm = 1000 m = 1 km

(d) 1 : 50 000

1 mm = 50 metres.
1 cm = 500 metre = ½ km

(e) 1 : 20 000

1 mm = 20 metre

(f) 1 : 10 000

Figure 5.6
Maps at different scales centred on The Open University at Walton Hall in Milton Keynes, Buckinghamshire: (a) 1 : 500 000; (b) 1 : 200 000; (c) 1 : 100 000; (d) 1 : 50 000; (e) 1 : 20 000; (f) 1 : 10 000.

1 mm : 10,000 mm
1 mm = 10,000 mm
= 10 metre.

But if you wished to build an extension to your house, your architect or surveyor would need to draw plans showing the precise position of the boundaries of your land, and would need to consult a much larger scale map, say 1 : 1 000. On the other hand, to look at the whole of the continent of Africa or the Pacific Ocean requires a much smaller scale, of the order 1 : 25 000 000.

▨   What is the range between the two scales 1 : 1 000 and 1 : 25 000 000?

■   Dividing 25 000 000 by 1 000 gives a factor of 25 000.

For most purposes, the range of distances of interest in everyday activities lies within these two extremes. In scientific studies, however, it is often necessary to work with distances that are many times larger or many times smaller than those we encounter in working with maps. To be able to do this means that we need a more compact way of talking about these extreme distances, one that is based on the metric system, but which extends the prefixes we use in both directions. Further, we need to be able to handle very large and very small numbers and for this a different notation is used, based on powers of ten and called scientific notation. We shall explore this in the next Section.

5.3 Powers of ten

In the previous Section, we looked at the various scales of maps that are appropriate for different requirements. These covered a range of roughly 25 000. But suppose we wished to loosen our ties to Earth and travel into space, what scales become appropriate then, for travelling to the Moon, to Mars, or even to the nearest star, Alpha Centauri? You can begin to understand the scales involved by looking at the pictures in Figures 5.7–5.16.* In this sequence of images, we shall be able to see the effect of undertaking a journey out into space, while all the time keeping our attention fixed on the same central spot.

Figure 5.7 shows an image with a field of view that is square, each side being one metre in length. It shows a man snoozing on a rug after a picnic. The picture you are looking at is 10 cm by 10 cm, exactly one-tenth the *linear* scale of the objects shown, that is 1:10. (Because each side of the square is one-tenth lifesize, the *area* is one-tenth multiplied by one-tenth, that is one-hundredth the size.) At this scale it is easy to see the various items such as books and magazines located near the man, but it is too restricted to show his woman companion sitting on the rug and reading a magazine.

If we move away from the picnic and expand the field of view to 10 m by 10 m, while still showing the image as a picture 10 cm by 10 cm, as in Figure 5.8, the scale changes to 1 : 100. In this picture, as in all the succeeding ones as we move farther and farther away, the rug remains at the centre of each image. The area occupied by the rug has become only a small fraction of the whole and the surrounding grass occupies most of the picture. At this scale, the woman, located at the lower left corner of the rug, can be seen, but only on close inspection.

*Figures 5.7- 5.20 are taken from the book *Powers of Ten* by Philip and Phylis Morrison and The Office of Charles and Ray Eames, Scientific American Books (1982) by kind permission of the publishers.

Figure 5.7
A man and a woman at a picnic in Chicago,
Illinois, USA. The scale is 1:10.

Figure 5.8
Image centred on the picnic at a scale of
1 : 100.

The couple are in a park in Chicago, on the shore of Lake Michigan, one of the five Great Lakes in the USA. In the next image, Figure 5.9, again with a field of view ten times larger than the previous one, so that the scale is now 1 : 1 000, it becomes apparent that the park is located between a busy road and a dock for private boats. By now, the details of the couple at their picnic have become indistinct.

Figure 5.9
Image centred on the picnic at a scale of 1 : 1 000.

After the next step in our journey, in Figure 5.10, Lake Michigan itself comes into view at the top right of the picture. The road, Lake Shore Drive, as its name implies, is seen to run along the edge of the lake. Various museums and the stadium known as Soldiers' Field are also visible. At the bottom right, the end of a runway of the local airport can be seen. In this picture, the scale has become 1 : 10 000. By now the couple and their picnic have disappeared totally.

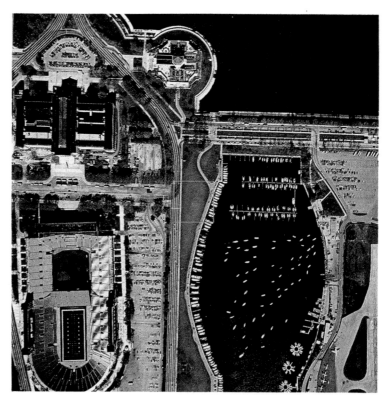

Figure 5.10
Image centred on the picnic at a scale of 1 : 10 000.

In Figure 5.11, the edge of the picture represents 10 000 m (10 km or approximately 6 miles). The lakeside park area has now become indistinct and only major features of the city of Chicago are visible, together with a larger section of Lake Michigan. The scale is now 1 : 100 000.

Figure 5.11
Image centred on the picnic at a scale of 1 : 100 000.

In Figure 5.12, the sides of the square represent 100 000 m or 100 km, approximately 60 miles. Here, the shape of the southern tip of Lake Michigan becomes clear, and much of the metropolitan area of greater Chicago can be seen. However, at this scale of 1 : 1 000 000 only the main roads can be made out, otherwise the picture just gives an impression of a large city.

Figure 5.12
Image centred on the picnic at a scale of 1 : 1 000 000.

Another ten times farther out, with the sides of the square in Figure 5.13 representing 1 000 000 m or 1 000 km, the Chicago area has become quite indistinct. The whole of Lake Michigan can now be seen, and the clouds in the lower atmosphere start to appear. The scale has by now reached 1:10 000 000.

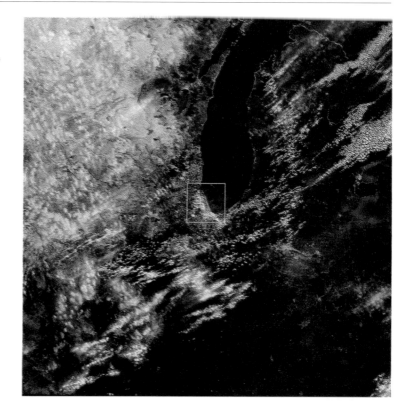

Figure 5.13
Image centred on the picnic at a scale of
1 : 10 000 000.

In Figure 5.14, even the giant Lake Michigan has become minute, and the spherical shape of the Earth itself at last begins to become apparent. The extensive array of clouds throughout the atmosphere is the most visible feature at this scale of 1 : 100 000 000, with the sides of the square representing 10 000 000 m, or 10 000 km.

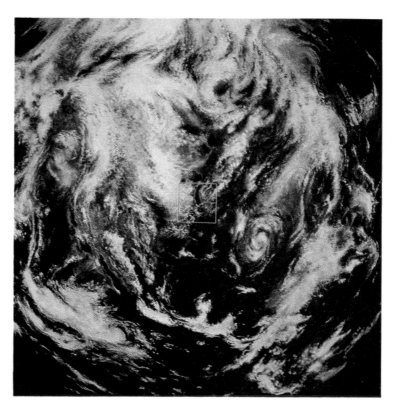

Figure 5.14
Image centred on the picnic at a scale of
1:100 000 000.

When the field of view is enlarged further, so that the sides of the square in Figure 5.15 now represent 100 000 000 m or 100 000 km, about 60 000 miles, the Earth has shrunk to a sphere just over 1 cm across, and the emptiness of the surrounding space is relieved only by the dim light of millions of stars. The scale in this picture has reached 1:1 000 000 000.

Figure 5.15
Image centred on the picnic at a scale of 1 : 1 000 000 000.

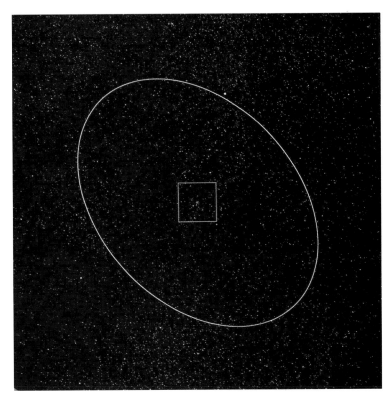

Finally, in Figure 5.16, when the field of view is enlarged just ten times more, to a square with sides representing 1 000 000 000 m or 1 000 000 km, the Earth has all but disappeared and the orbit of the Moon can now be seen. The scale now is 1 : 10 000 000 000, that is one to ten thousand million, or one to ten billion.

Figure 5.16
Image centred on the picnic at a scale of 1 : 10 000 000 000.

It would be possible to continue this process until we reached a point that would correspond to the edge of the Universe as we presently know it, but for our purposes we have gone far enough. Clearly, as we have moved from one picture to the next, the scale has increased tenfold; we often say it has increased by a factor of ten. This has involved adding a zero both to the distance represented by the edge of the 10 cm square and to the scale involved. As the numbers have increased, the number of zeros has become quite large. In Figure 5.16, the scale has reached 1:10 000 000 000; had we continued to the limit mentioned above, the scale would have reached a truly astronomical 1:100 000 000 000 000 000 000 000 000! Clearly, just handling such numbers becomes a burden in itself, and so a shorthand notation becomes necessary simply for practical reasons. The notation used is called **powers of ten** or, more correctly, **scientific notation**.

Take the number 100. This can be thought of as 10×10, which we can write as 10^2: the two indicates that two 10s have to be multiplied together to give the number represented.

- How would you write the number 1 000 using this notation?

- Because 1 000 can be written as $10 \times 10 \times 10$, then this would be 10^3.

The number written as a superscript to the right of the figure 10 is called the power, hence the term powers-of-ten. So 10^2 is 'ten to the power two' (though frequently also referred to as 'ten squared') and 10^3 is 'ten to the power three' (frequently also referred to as 'ten cubed'). Note that an easy way to work out the power in these cases is to count the number of zeros. The number of zeros is in fact the same as the power. While there may seem to be little obvious advantage in writing 10^3 for the number 1 000, for larger numbers, such as 10 000 000 000, it is clearly much more concise.

- How would you write the number 10 000 000 000 using scientific (powers of ten) notation?

- Because there are ten zeros in 10 000 000 000, it can be written as $10 \times 10 \times 10 \times 10 \times 10 \times 10 \times 10 \times 10 \times 10 \times 10$ (ten tens multiplied together), so this would be 10^{10}.

If conciseness were the only advantage in using scientific notation, it would still be a useful system. However, it has a further big advantage. Consider the multiplication $100 \times 1 000$: the answer is pretty straightforward, that is 100 000.

- How would you write the same multiplication using scientific notation?

- Because 100 is 10^2, 1 000 is 10^3 and 100 000 is 10^5, the multiplication would be written as follows: $10^2 \times 10^3 = 10^5$.

- Do you notice a relationship between the powers of the two numbers multiplied together and the power of the answer?

- The power of the answer (5) is obtained by *adding* the powers of the two numbers being multiplied together (2 and 3).

So when two numbers that are multiples of ten are multiplied together, you can obtain the answer by adding the powers. This also works when more than two such numbers are multiplied together.

Question 13 Use scientific notation to work out the answer to the following multiplication: $10 \times 1\,000 \times 100$.

Scientific notation is not limited just to numbers that are whole multiples of ten. Consider the two numbers $3\,625$ and 284. The first number can be thought of as being 362.5×10, or 36.25×100, or $3.625 \times 1\,000$: using scientific notation these would become 362.5×10, or 36.25×10^2, or 3.625×10^3, respectively. Generally, when using scientific notation, numbers are expressed in the form $number \times 10^{power}$ where the number is between 1 and 9.999..., and the power is a whole number. In other words, we would generally write $3\,625$ as 3.625×10^3. Using the same rule, we would write 284 as 2.84×10^2.

Question 14 Use scientific notation to work out the answer to the multiplication $3\,625 \times 284$.

Often in science, technology or everyday life, we need to get some idea of the approximate relationship between the size of one thing and the size of another. It is very useful to use the powers-of-ten concept for this and to think in terms of **orders of magnitude**. Consider the carrying capacity of a Boeing 747 aircraft, for example, which can readily accommodate in excess of 400 passengers, and a commuter aircraft holding about 40 passengers. Clearly the former has ten times the capacity of the latter, that is 10^1 (ten to the power one). This is often expressed slightly differently, and the carrying capacity of the 747 is said to be one order of magnitude greater. So an order of magnitude represents a factor of (approximately) ten. Compared with a private aircraft capable of carrying just four people, the capacity of the 747 would be said to be two orders of magnitude greater, because 100 is 10^2 (ten to the power two).

The concept of 'order of magnitude' is more often used to give an approximate relationship between values: for example, the distance between London and Aberdeen is about 490 miles and the distance between London and Milton Keynes is about 55 miles; saying that the former is an order of magnitude greater than the latter is acceptable for many purposes.

5.4 A microscopic view

In the previous Section, we undertook an imaginary journey out into space, examining the enlarged field of view as we proceeded. But suppose we did just the opposite and moved in closer, so that instead of the edges of the square that bounds our view being 100 cm or 1 m long, it becomes just 10 cm along each side.

▪ What would the scale become in this case?

◾ Because the sizes of the pictures are 10 cm by 10 cm, the scale would be 1 : 1, and the image is lifesize.

Figure 5.17 shows this situation, where the image is now little more than the back of the man's hand as he sleeps on the rug after the picnic. As with your own hand, the skin and underlying veins can be clearly seen.

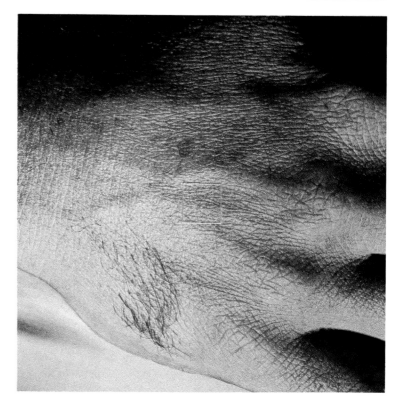

Figure 5.17
Image of the back of the man's hand. The scale is 1 : 1 or lifesize.

If we reduce the field of view by a further factor of ten, the sides of the square now represent a length of 1 cm and the scale becomes 1 : 0.1. The image in Figure 5.18 is of skin as seen through a magnifying glass.

Figure 5.18
Image of the skin on the back of the man's hand at a scale of 1 : 0.1.

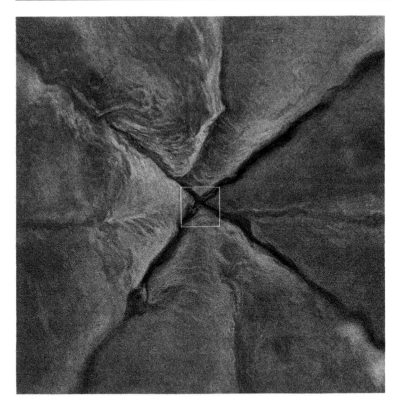

Reducing the field of view still further, so that the image has sides that represent just 0.1 cm or 1 mm, the view in Figure 5.19 is akin to that seen through a microscope. The image has been enlarged 100 times in each dimension compared with lifesize, so that the area examined is just one-tenthousandth of the lifesize image in Figure 5.17. The scale is now 1 : 0.01.

Figure 5.19
Image of the back of the man's hand at a scale of 1 : 0.01.

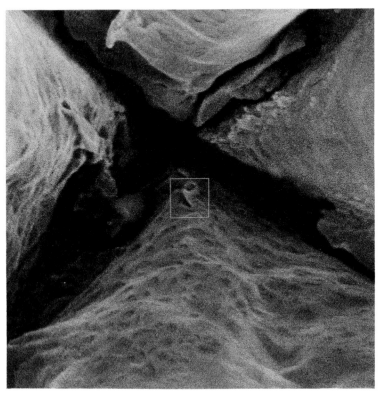

Continuing the process, Figure 5.20 shows an image with sides representing 0.1 mm. Such an enlargement requires the use of an instrument called an electron microscope, which is capable of producing much greater enlargements than a microscope that uses light. Here the scale has become 1 : 0.001.

Figure 5.20
Image of the back of the man's hand at a scale of 1 : 0.001.

It would be possible to continue the process of reducing the field of view by ever-greater enlargements, but to do so at this stage would be to pre-empt much of what we shall be introducing you to later in this Book. Let's just say here that much of the Course is concerned with a scale where the imaginary field of view has sides of 0.000 001 mm, a scale of 1 : 0.000 000 01. It is scales such as these that are meant when we refer to the sub-microscopic scale of matter.

As with large numbers in the previous Section, very small numbers are cumbersome to write out and it would be much more convenient if we could use a powers-of-ten type notation as a shorthand. The question is, can we extend the notation above to small numbers as well as large ones, or does there need to be a different notation?

Consider the following multiplication:

$$100\,000 \times 0.1 = 10\,000$$

If we write the large numbers using scientific notation, then the multiplication looks like this:

$$10^5 \times 0.1 = 10^4$$

Remembering that when we multiply numbers, we need to add their powers, we could represent 0.1 using scientific notation if we wrote it using a negative exponent as 1.0×10^{-1} or just 10^{-1}. This would be consistent, since positive powers tell us the number of zeros to add to get the number. For negative powers, it is easier to look at the position of the decimal point in the number we wish to express using powers of ten. To express 0.1 in the form *number* × 10^{power} we need to move the decimal point *one* place to the *right* to get a number between 1 and 9.999..., in this case 1.0. So 0.1 is 1.0×10^{-1}. The power is the number of places we have to move the decimal point, with a minus sign in front.

It is perhaps easier to see how this works with a different number, say 0.24. To express this in scientific notation, using the rule about moving the decimal point, and remembering that the number in *number* × 10^{power} needs to be in the range between 1 and 9.999, we have to move the decimal place one place to the right: $0.24 \rightarrow 2.4 \times 10^{-1}$.

- Using this new rule, write down 0.002 using scientific notation.

- We need to move the decimal point *three* places to the right ($0.002 \rightarrow 0.02 \times 10^{-1} \rightarrow 0.2 \times 10^{-2} \rightarrow 2.0 \times 10^{-3}$), so this would be written as 2.0×10^{-3}.

- Now write down 0.000 001 using scientific notation.

- To do this, we need to move the decimal point *six* places to the right ($0.000\,001 \rightarrow 0.000\,01 \times 10^{-1} \rightarrow 0.000\,1 \times 10^{-2} \rightarrow 0.001 \times 10^{-3} \rightarrow 0.01 \times 10^{-4} \rightarrow 0.1 \times 10^{-5} \rightarrow 1.0 \times 10^{-6}$), so the answer is 1.0×10^{-6}.

Conversely, to express a number in scientific notation as a decimal, we just reverse the process: the power tells us the number of places to move the decimal point to the *left*.

■   Write down 3.5×10^{-4} as a decimal number.

■   Since the power is -4, we need to move the decimal point four places to the left ($3.5 \times 10^{-4} \rightarrow 0.35 \times 10^{-3} \rightarrow 0.035 \times 10^{-2} \rightarrow 0.0035 \times 10^{-1} \rightarrow 0.00035$), so the answer is 0.000 35.

The rule about moving the decimal point also works for large numbers, but the opposite way round because these involve *positive* powers. So converting from a decimal into scientific notation for large numbers involves moving the decimal point to the *left*, and to convert scientific notation into a decimal number involves moving the decimal point to the *right*.

■   Write down 3.5×10^3 as a decimal number.

■   Since the power is 3, we need to move the decimal place three places to the right ($3.5 \times 10^3 \rightarrow 35 \times 10^2 \rightarrow 350 \times 10^1 \rightarrow 3500$), so the answer is 3 500.

So we can represent large numbers by using positive powers, and small numbers by using negative powers. What about a zero power? Does this have any meaning? Think about the following multiplication:

$$10 \times 0.1 = 1.0$$

If we write the numbers on the left of the equals sign using scientific notation, then the multiplication looks like this:

$$(1.0 \times 10^1) \times (1.0 \times 10^{-1}) = 1.0$$

Remembering once again that when we multiply numbers, we need to add their powers, we could represent the number 1 using scientific notation if we wrote it using an exponent of zero as 1.0×10^0. This may seem an odd idea, and a little difficult to grasp, but it makes for a consistent rule because it means we need to move the decimal point no places to the right or to the left, leaving the answer as 1.0.

The units of length in Section 5.1 used the extended notation that 1 km equals 1 000 m, 1 cm equals 0.01 m, and 1 mm equals 0.001 m. Now that you are familiar with scientific notation, we can represent these more concisely using exponents. Additionally, we can introduce a couple more units that we shall be using frequently during the Course when discussing very small distances, down to 0.000 001 mm or less. These various units of length are shown in Table 5.2.

Table 5.2 SI units of length

Prefix	Size	Symbol
kilometre	10^3 m	km
metre	1 m (standard)	m
centimetre	10^{-2} m	cm
millimetre	10^{-3} m	mm
micrometre[a]	10^{-6} m	µm[b]
nanometre	10^{-9} m	nm
picometre	10^{-12} m	pm

[a] The unit micrometre is sometimes referred to by the name micron.
[b] The symbol for micrometre makes use of the Greek letter µ, transliterated as 'mu' and pronounced 'mew'.

Negative powers are also useful for certain units. Consider the number 0.1: as we have seen, this is represented as 10^{-1}. But 0.1 expressed as a fraction is 1/10, or $1 \div 10^1$. We use the same principle for some units, such as that of speed. The SI unit of speed is metres per second, which can be written as metres/second or metres $\div$ second. Since, as we have just seen, dividing a number (or a unit) by a positive power gives a negative power, this can also be expressed as metres second^{-1}, or, in symbols, $m\,s^{-1}$.

The use of scientific notation, based on powers of ten, provides us not only with a very useful shorthand way of writing very large and very small numbers, but also with a means of manipulating any number more conveniently. In learning about powers of ten, we have also taken the opportunity to notice the different sizes of things both on Earth and to a limited extent in space. This understanding of the scale of matter is fundamental to any study of science or any one of its sub-divisions, and it will be a constant theme as we progress through the Course.

Summary of Chapter 5

Distances in the UK used to be measured using the Imperial system in miles, yards, feet and inches. For scientific purposes and now for general use, the metric or SI system is used, based on the metre. The metre was determined by comparison with a standard length bar kept in Paris, but is now defined in terms of the speed of light in a vacuum. Larger and smaller units are defined using standard prefixes: examples are the kilometre (10^3 m) and the millimetre (10^{-3} m).

Through considering the various uses made of maps, the concept of scale was introduced. For most purposes, maps with scales between 1:1 000 and 1:25 000 000 are adequate. However, in scientific studies it is frequently necessary to work with scales much larger or much smaller than those appropriate for maps.

In order to handle the numbers required for large and small scales, a more powerful notation called scientific notation is needed. An imaginary journey out from the Earth into space introduced the method of handling very large numbers using positive powers. The converse journey into 'inner space' by zooming into a man's hand extended the concept to negative powers of ten.

Approximate relationships between objects of different sizes are often needed and, for this purpose, comparison of their sizes expressed as a power of ten is useful. This is called an order of magnitude comparison. Consistency in applying the rules for positive and negative powers leads to the conclusion that 10^0 equals 1.

Question 15 When drawing up plans for remodelled kitchens, designers frequently use a scale of $1:20$. What size would a kitchen measuring 3.6 m by 4.2 m be on such a plan?

Question 16 Use scientific notation to work out the answer to the following multiplication: 0.25×0.04.

Chapter 6
The three states of matter

6.1 What is matter?

The physical world is very complex indeed, but does this complexity arise because nature is intrinsically complicated or does it conceal an underlying simplicity? The idea that complex things can be understood in terms of combinations of simple things is a very persuasive and seductive idea for scientists. A prime example of this is in understanding the structure of matter.

■ The world is constructed of matter. What do you think is meant by the word 'matter' in that statement?

■ Matter means the physical material of the Universe and all that is in it, both animate and inanimate.

So far, we have used the term **matter** without really defining it. The problem is that definitions of fundamental properties, such as matter, are difficult to frame exactly, and they usually end up referring to something else that itself needs definition. One definition is that matter occupies space (Box 6.1). Perhaps a more useful definition, though, is that matter is something that has **mass**. An object with mass has a resistance to being moved. The mass of an object is a property of the object that is unaffected by changes in temperature, pressure, position in space or anything else. We could say that it is an intrinsic property of the object. Additionally, anything with mass is attracted to anything else with mass. We call this attraction the **gravitational force**, or **gravity**. We have, in this way, defined matter in terms of a measurable quantity – mass.

The difference between mass and weight is one that often causes confusion. Your weight is a measure of the force that you are exerting on a weighing machine. The amount by which a spring extends, when you hang something from it, is a measure of the weight of that something. The weight of an object is directly related to its mass through gravity. On Earth, our weight is due to the large mass of the Earth attracting us towards itself; Newton's apple fell to the ground because the Earth was attracting it.

Let's compare two objects: one is a small gold bar with a volume of $50\,cm^3$; the other is a small silver bar also with a volume of $50\,cm^3$. The gold bar would have a mass of about 960 g but the silver one would have a mass of only about 520 g. There is nearly twice as much mass in the gold as there is in the silver. But how do we measure mass?

Just as the standard of length was originally defined in terms of a standard metre, mass is defined in terms of a standard kilogram. The standard of mass is a cylinder made of the platinum–iridium mixture used for the standard metre and also kept at the International Bureau of Weights and Measures at Sèvres. However, while new more accurate standards have been defined for length, this cylinder is still the standard of mass and is internationally agreed to have a mass of one kilogram. All measurements of mass derive from this standard.

Box 6.1 Matter in three dimensions

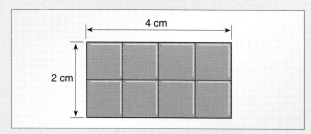

Figure 6.1
A rectangle with sides 2 cm by 4 cm.

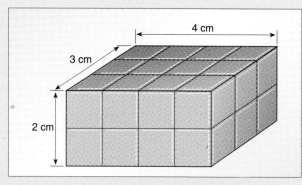

Figure 6.2
A rectangular solid with sides 2 cm by 3 cm by 4 cm.

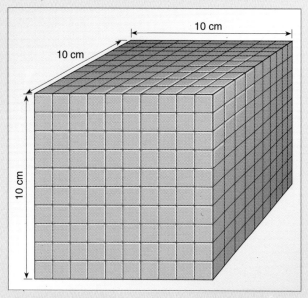

Figure 6.3
A cube with sides 10 cm by 10 cm by 10 cm. Its volume is 1 000 cm³ or one litre.

In everyday life, we frequently come across the measurement of length, area and volume. If you go for a journey, the distance between your starting point and destination is a length, usually measured in miles. Buying electrical flex to fit to a new appliance involves a length, usually in metres. Measuring the area of a room for a new carpet used to be done in terms of square yards, but now more usually it is in square metres. Farmers are concerned with how many acres (or hectares) of ground to plant with a particular crop. As for volumes, milk and beer are bought in pints (in the UK), and petrol used to be bought by the gallon, but now by the litre.

As you may recall from Chapter 5, in science the standard (SI) unit of length is the metre, with its various sub-units. The area of a rectangle is obtained by multiplying the lengths of two adjacent sides together. The sides of the rectangle shown in Figure 6.1 are 2 cm and 4 cm, respectively, so the area is 2 cm × 4 cm = 8 cm² (square centimetres or centimetres squared). Any surface, even if irregularly shaped, has an area that can be determined, and is expressed in the same square units (square metres or one of the sub-units).

Similarly, a rectangular solid of sides 2 cm by 3 cm by 4 cm (Figure 6.2) will have a volume of 2 cm × 3 cm × 4 cm = 24 cm³ (cubic centimetres or centimetres cubed). Any object, whatever its shape, has a volume that can be determined, and is expressed in the same cubic units.

The volume of a cube with sides 10 cm by 10 cm by 10 cm (Figure 6.3) is given a special name, a litre (symbol l). Because a litre has a volume of 1 000 cm³, the sub-unit of a millilitre (symbol ml), which is equal to 1 cm³, is often used interchangeably with the latter.

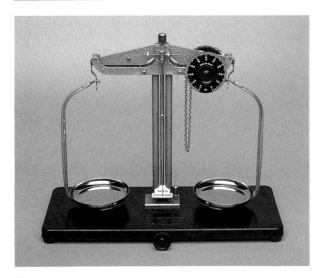

Figure 6.4
A simple laboratory beam balance of *ca.*1970s vintage. The sample to be weighed is placed on the left-hand pan, and 'weights' are added to the right-hand one until the beam is balanced. This allows the mass to be determined to the nearest gram. By turning the calibrated knob, the amount of chain hanging can be varied, which allows the mass to be determined to the nearest 0.1 g. Much more sophisticated beam balances are able to weigh to an accuracy of 1 μg. — $10^{-6} g = 0.000\ 001\ g$

There are two main types of balance used for determining masses. One type is shown in Figure 6.4; this relies on comparing the mass of the object of interest with the mass of a set of standard masses. The object of which the mass is to be measured is placed on one pan of the balance. Standard masses are then added to the other until the beam of the balance is 'balanced', that is it lies horizontally. In this case the attraction of the Earth for both pans and their contents is equal, and so the masses are the same. The second type of balance relies on some other effect to measure the attraction of the Earth: older balances used the extension of a spring; more modern balances (Figure 6.5) found in laboratories, supermarkets, and even kitchens, rely on a transducer that converts the strength of the Earth's gravity into an electric current that is then shown on a digital display. Both the spring balance and the more modern electronic balance have to be calibrated with standard masses.

The confusion between weight and mass referred to above arises because both the processes we have been describing for the measurement of mass are called 'weighing', both in everyday language and by scientists. The confusion is compounded because the standard masses are generally referred to as 'weights'. However, scientists distinguish between mass and weight as follows. The mass is the intrinsic property of the object and is measured in units of kilograms or a sub-unit (gram, milligram, etc.) as we have described above. The weight is the force experienced by a given mass and is measured using the SI unit of force which is called the newton (named after Isaac Newton, and given the symbol N). The weight of an object depends on its location. The standard kilogram mass on the surface of the Earth experiences a force due to gravity of about 9.8 N (9.85 N near the Poles and 9.75 N near the Equator), *and this is therefore its weight.*

Figure 6.5
A modern electronic balance for use in a laboratory capable of reading to 0.000 1 g (0.1 mg). Accurate balances such as these are provided with a standard mass and a built-in program to recalibrate when necessary. There is a need for recalibration for use in different parts of the world because the Earth's gravity varies from place to place. One reason for this is that the Earth is not perfectly spherical. Consequently, a balance calibrated in London would give an erroneous reading in Bombay unless it was recalibrated using a standard mass.

Throughout the Course, we shall be concerned with mass rather than weight. However, for brevity and convenience, we shall follow common practice and use the term 'weighing' when we really mean 'determining the mass'. Next time you stand on the bathroom scales and read off the number of pounds (or possibly kilograms) indicated, whatever your feelings about the value displayed, you will at least know that you are measuring your mass and not your weight!

So far, we have been concentrating on just one property of matter, its mass. But it is clear from even a most cursory look at your surroundings that matter takes on an incredible diversity of forms, materials and colours. Yet, as you will see as you proceed through the Course, this amazing variety can be understood in terms of a limited set of building blocks and a few simple ideas as to how these interact.

Unfortunately, even though there is a relatively small number of building blocks, their nature and constitution are outside our direct experience, not least because of their sub-microscopic size. But we need to be able to visualize them in order to understand how they behave. So we build a bridge between what we think these sub-microscopic entities are like and what we do know about. In other words we make models. As you may recall from Chapter 2, these are not necessarily solid, physical models, they can also be ideas or conceptual models. You will use both kinds of model during the Course. You may even invent your own to help you to understand some of the theories you will meet.

We shall begin by looking at the three main states of matter – solid, liquid and gas – and we shall examine the properties of each of the three states. To make matters as simple as possible, we shall illustrate the discussion using the properties of pure substances, by which we mean a single pure form of matter. For example, we shall look at what happens when a substance changes from one state to another, such as when ice melts to form liquid water. In Chapter 7 we shall go on to develop the model of matter that we shall be using throughout the Course. And then in Chapter 8, we shall apply this model to explaining the behaviour of the three states of matter described in this Chapter.

6.2 Is it a solid? Is it a liquid? Is it a gas?

What we are going to do in this Section is to classify matter according to its physical state. Later, we shall explore the relationship between the physical state of a substance and its fundamental structure. For the time being, let's concentrate on what we can experience. Things around us have form, and we classify those forms in terms of the solid, liquid and gaseous states (Figure 6.6).

▪ Look around you and think about the states of things nearby. Can you find three solids, three liquids and three gases? Do not be concerned about the *composition* of the things you choose (what they are made of); at the moment we are only interested in their form or state.

▪ The solids are easy. Some examples are: wood, coins, this book, shoes, tables, chairs, pencils, computers and teapots. The liquids are also quite easy. Tea is liquid, water is liquid and so is petrol; other liquids are paint brush cleaner, olive oil and wine. The gases are a little more difficult unless you have already studied some science. Here are some you may know. Natural gas (mostly methane) is used as a fuel for cookers and the

generation of electricity in some power stations. If you go camping, you probably use canisters of butane gas for cooking. The gas in lemonade and other 'fizzy' drinks is carbon dioxide. Air is a gas, a mixture of roughly 78% nitrogen, 21% oxygen and 1% other gases, notably argon and carbon dioxide. Lighter-than-air balloons contain a gas called helium. However, what Americans call 'gas' (as in 'step on the gas!') is what the British call petrol (a liquid).

Activity 9
Solids, liquids and gases

Try to frame definitions of solids, liquids and gases, in terms of your experience of their physical characteristics.

Some definitions for you to compare with yours are given in the Comments on Activities at the end of the book.

Figure 6.6
The three states of matter – solid, liquid and gas.

The descriptions given in the answer to Activity 9 seem like good working definitions, so let's see how some common materials measure up to them. If we take a stone as the first example of a solid then everything seems fine. It has a shape of its own that does not change if it is transferred from a flat plate to a deep dish. If you want to change the shape of a solid then a force must be applied (Figure 6.7).

Figure 6.7
Force needs to be applied to change the shape of a solid!

When the stone is broken into pieces the total volume does not change and neither does the total mass.

■   How might you verify the first part of this statement?

■   As you read in Chapter 2, Archimedes is supposed to have been in his bath when he leapt out and cried 'Eureka!'. He had recognized that if a solid is fully immersed in water, or any other liquid, then the volume of water that is displaced is exactly the same as the volume of the solid. This means that you could measure (in a graduated container) the volume of water displaced by the whole stone. Then you could break the stone into pieces, being sure to save every bit, put the pieces into the measuring vessel and note again how much water is displaced. The two volumes will be the same (Figure 6.8).

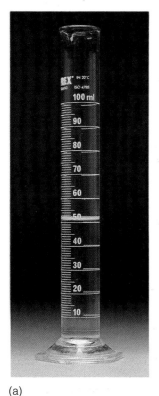
(a)

(b)

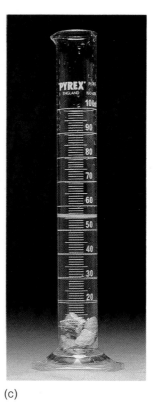
(c)

Figure 6.8
(a) A measuring cylinder containing water; (b) the same measuring cylinder with a stone immersed in the water; (c) the measuring cylinder with the stone fragments immersed in the water.

■   How might you verify the second part of the above statement – that the mass of the stone remains the same when it is broken?

■   This is even simpler. It just involves weighing the stone before and after it is smashed to pieces.

Other solids, such as your tea or coffee cup, are solid in the same way as a stone is solid. They feel solid and unless you do something drastic to them they are always the same shape. Not everything falls quite so nicely into the solids class, however. Think about and if possible look at some talcum powder. Talc is a natural mineral that is ground into a very fine powder, which is used for its absorbent properties.

Talc is used for its excellent slip. However it has poor absorbent properties for oil or water. For this reason Talcum powder, the cosmetic is a mixture of compounds, often including magnesium carbonate to improve absorbency.

■ Look back at the definitions of states and try to think what might be ambiguous about talcum powder.

■ Talcum powder will take the shape of its container and if the container shape changes so will the shape of the talcum powder. If you pour the talcum powder out of its container it appears to flow rather like a liquid.

There are other powders that behave even more like liquids. With some of these, if you put them in a dish and gently shake it, the surface has waves on it, just like water. These, like talcum powder, are still said to be solids. So what is making them solids? You may have already thought of the answer, which is to do with looking more closely at the powders. Powders are made up of millions of tiny solid particles, each of which is recognizable as a solid. You may have to use a magnifying glass or a microscope to see the particles, but they are there. A powder is not continuous like a liquid, it is lumpy to a greater or lesser extent.

From the point of view of easy classification, there is at least one other problem material in every home: glass. It feels solid. (I first wrote that it looks solid and then I looked through the window and realized that it didn't look anything at all.) It sounds solid. When you knock gently on a window it resists your attempt to change its shape. These are all definite characteristics of a solid and in our experience glass is a solid. At normal temperatures, glass can also behave like a liquid. In the cathedral at Chartres in France there are some very beautiful stained-glass windows (Figure 6.9). In the course of restoration work, it was discovered that some of the windows were wafer thin at the top and ten to twenty times thicker at the bottom. Over five or six hundred years, the effect of gravity had caused the glass to flow. This is another illustration of the importance of framing a definition clearly and understanding its limits. Glass behaves like a liquid only on a time-scale of hundreds of years. On our own time-scale of seconds to decades glass behaves like a solid. There is no problem with this. In science, we are used to referring to a particular time-scale and recognizing that our definitions may be dependent on time.

Figure 6.9
Stained glass window in the cathedral at Chartres, France.

Although it is not such a popular plaything any more you may be familiar with 'silly putty' or 'potty putty'. It's a material that bounces, but also stretches and, if left long enough, flows to take the shape of its container. We would generally say, with an unknown material, that if it bounces it's a solid and if it flows it's a liquid. Silly putty is rather like glass but on a much shorter time-scale. In the time-scale of a bounce, which is a fraction of a second, the putty behaves like a solid. Over a few hours the putty behaves as if it were a liquid. Again there is no conflict. The answer to the direct question 'is it a liquid or is it a solid?' would have to be 'it is both, but which set of properties it shows depends on the time-scale'.

There are lots of substances that are completely and unambiguously liquid. By and large we recognize them rather easily. Tea is a liquid, so is the milk we put in it (but we shall look again at milk in a little while). Washing-up liquid is even called a liquid, so we know that it is one. But suppose you were to blow a bubble with washing-up liquid or a child's bubble mixture. Think about what you would see if you looked very closely at the bubble. It has air, a gas, in the middle, but what about the outside – the skin? Is it a solid? Not really. If it is a liquid, why isn't it flowing and taking the shape of a container? There are quite a lot of materials that do not fit readily into our solid, liquid and gas categories and a soap film is one of them. Materials like soap films (and liquid crystals of the type in your watch display, to be discussed in Book 4) have been classified as 'soft matter', and their study has led to new discoveries about the structure of matter.

Gases are usually more straightforward in that something either completely occupies its container, even if the volume of the container is changed, or it does not. We have less direct experience of gases than the other two main states. We cannot see the common gases. As you may recall from earlier, the difficulty of recognizing that gases are another form of matter was a major stumbling block for the early chemists. We can experience air by feeling the wind blow on us, and we can experience the effect of lack of air by holding our breath. The only time that a colourless gas can be 'seen' is in the form of bubbles in fizzy drinks or elsewhere. Not all gases are colourless, though. Chlorine, a gas used in the First World War for its deadly poisonous effects, is pale green; nitrogen dioxide, one of the pollutants arising from car exhausts, is brown (Figure 6.10).

Figure 6.10
A view towards central Los Angeles from the South showing the trapping of pollutants. The brown colour is due, in part, to nitrogen dioxide.

Box 6.2 Temperature and pressure

You are doubtless familiar with the concepts of temperature and pressure from weather reports if nowhere else. You may also have noticed that for some years, the temperature was given using two different scales, in terms of degrees Celsius and degrees Fahrenheit; the latter has now largely fallen into disuse, although it is still used in the USA. Until 1948, the Celsius scale was known as the centigrade scale; it was then renamed as the Celsius scale after the Swedish astronomer Anders Celsius (1701–1744) who originally devised the centigrade scale. On the Celsius scale, the melting temperature of ice at normal atmospheric pressure (see below) is 0 degrees (written as 0 °C) and the boiling temperature of water, also at normal atmospheric pressure, is 100 degrees (100 °C).

The Fahrenheit scale is a temperature scale on which the normal melting temperature of ice is 32 degrees (written as 32 °F) and the normal boiling temperature of water is 212 degrees (212 °F). It was devised in the early eighteenth century by Daniel Fahrenheit (1689–1736), a Dutch instrument maker who constructed the first successful mercury–glass thermometers. When the scale was devised, the lowest temperature reachable in the laboratory using an ice-salt mixture was taken to be 0 °F.

Although much lower temperatures are reachable and indeed are commonplace in the polar regions, there is a limit to how cold something can be: this is now called **absolute zero**. On the Celsius scale, absolute zero is −273.15 °C. Scientists have managed to reach within less than a millionth of a degree of absolute zero, but never absolute zero itself. However, there does not seem to be an upper limit to temperature; the highest temperatures known, in the centres of stars, are many millions of degrees Celsius. In this Course, temperatures are always given using the Celsius scale.

Pressure is defined as the application of force over a given area. The SI unit of pressure is the pascal (named after the French scientist Blaise Pascal (1623–1662), and given the symbol Pa): a pascal is a force of one newton (Section 6.1) applied over an area of one square metre (Figure 6.11). A pressure of 100 000 (10^5) Pa is equal to one bar. You may be familiar with the air pressure required to inflate car tyres; these are usually measured in pounds per square inch (p.s.i.). A typical value would be about 30 p.s.i. or about 2 bars; most garage air-lines have gauges marked with both scales.

The atmospheric pressure is given in weather reports in units of millibars (10^{-3} bar). One bar or 1 000 millibars is very roughly the average pressure of the atmosphere, so when a high-pressure area is forecast values of 1 030 millibars would be typical, whereas values of 970 millibars would be typical if a low pressure area is on the way (Figure 6.12). For scientific purposes, **normal atmospheric pressure** is taken to be a pressure of one bar.

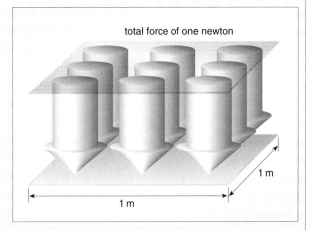

Figure 6.11
A pressure of one pascal – a force of one newton applied over an area of one square metre.

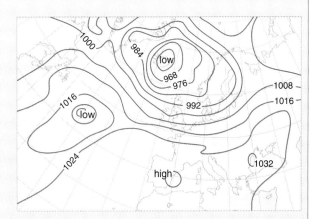

Figure 6.12
A typical weather map of the United Kingdom and northeast mainland Europe.

6.3 Changes of state

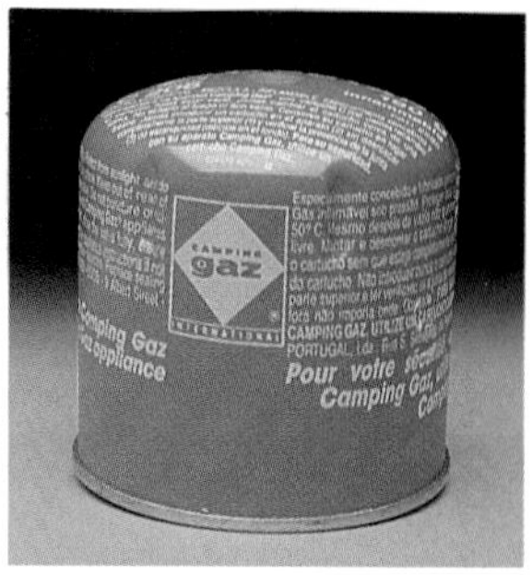

If you go camping or have a gas-fired barbecue, have you ever wondered why the canisters or cylinders of butane gas used for cooking (Figure 6.13) sound as though they contain a liquid when they are shaken? You may also have noticed that, after use, the canister is cold to the touch and there is often a film of liquid water (so-called condensation) near the top. The reason is that the butane in the canister is in the liquid form because it is under pressure. As the butane emerges through the burner nozzle, it changes from the liquid form to a gas, a change that requires energy. The necessary energy is taken from the liquid butane and its container. The result is that they become cold, which leads to the condensation of moisture from the atmosphere on to the canister.

This change from liquid butane to gas is called a **change of state**. The discussion in the previous Section concerned the form of substances under normal conditions, that is atmospheric pressure and room temperature. If the pressure or temperature is increased or decreased, then a change of state can occur.

Figure 6.13
A butane canister of the type used when camping.

- What is the most familiar example of a substance that can easily be changed from one physical state (solid, liquid or gas) to another?

- Water is the obvious choice (Figure 6.14). You can make ice from water in a freezer. In the winter, lakes freeze over. When you boil a kettle or a pan of water, some of the water is turned into a gas (steam) and if you leave it long enough all of the water will boil away.

Figure 6.14
Winter scene with ice, water and steam.

Note that, though strictly steam is gaseous water which is actually invisible, the term is also used to describe the whitish clouds that can be seen which are actually very small droplets of liquid water in the atmosphere.

- In the burning match experiment, did you make any observation that could be interpreted in terms of a change of state?

- When the match was held close to the tumbler of cold water, a liquid appeared on the glass. This liquid is actually water and it is a chemical product of combustion. In the hot flame the water is formed as a gas, which condenses on contact with the cold surface.

Another example of water condensation occurs when a car is started. If you look at a car's exhaust just after the engine has started, you will see a liquid dripping out of the pipe. This is water formed by combustion of the petrol which then condenses in the cold pipe. When the hot exhaust gases heat the pipe sufficiently, the water no longer condenses and it is released into the atmosphere as a gas. (On very cold days, condensation of the water can still be seen as a cloud behind the vehicle.)

The state of a material depends on the conditions. If heated sufficiently strongly, most solids will change to a liquid, the process called **melting**. The temperature at which a substance melts at normal atmospheric pressure is called its **normal melting temperature**. Water is no exception. Ice melts at a temperature of 0 °C (at normal atmospheric pressure) to give liquid water. So, if left at temperatures higher than 0 °C, ice will melt, for example an ice cube in a glass at normal room temperature.

Similarly, if water is left in an open dish, it will eventually disappear, owing to the process called **evaporation**. What has happened is that, over a period of time, the liquid has been converted into a gas. The conversion of a liquid into a gas is also often called **vaporization**. The terms evaporation and vaporization are frequently used interchangeably. Initially vaporization occurs at the surface of the liquid. When a liquid is heated, the rate of vaporization is increased. If the heating is sufficiently strong, eventually a temperature is reached where vaporization occurs not just at the surface but throughout the bulk of the liquid as well. When this happens, the liquid is said to **boil**. The temperature at which a substance boils at normal atmospheric pressure is called its **normal boiling temperature**. Water boils when it reaches a temperature of 100 °C (at normal atmospheric pressure). Taking as an example a pan of water on a stove, the temperature of the water never exceeds 100 °C however high the setting of the control, but the rate at which the water vaporizes is faster than when a lower setting is used.

One question that you could legitimately ask is 'How do you know that it is just a change of state when water freezes? Could it be that ice and water are different *substances* rather than just different forms of the same thing?' That is a question that you could think about for a long time without being sure of the answer. It has to be answered by practical experiment. Later, we shall show you that liquid water and ice do indeed have the same chemical constitution and are different physical forms of the same substance. Usually, you can assume that if something changes its state under a particular set of conditions (e.g. temperature or pressure), and if that change is reversible, then it is simply a physical change and the substance does not change into another substance.

In most cases, as a substance is heated it expands. The most graphic illustration of this is a thermometer (Figure 6.15). For solids and liquids, the expansion is relatively small. A cube of aluminium, with sides of 10 cm at 20 °C, has a volume of 1 000 cm^3 (10 cm × 10 cm × 10 cm). When heated to 660 °C, just below the normal melting temperature of aluminium, it would have a volume of approximately 1 050 cm^3. This represents an expansion of 5% over a temperature range of 640 Celsius degrees. Usually on melting, an additional expansion takes place and the liquid formed is less dense than the solid. For example, a solid aluminium cube with a volume of 1 050 cm^3 at 660 °C would give approximately 1 130 cm^3 of liquid aluminium on melting. (Note that these figures relate only to aluminium; other substances would expand to different extents.) However, despite the expansion on heating being relatively small, it is none the less very important, and large structures such as bridges are built with small gaps to allow for expansion.

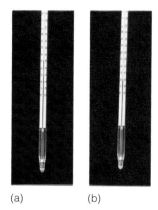

(a)   (b)

Figure 6.15
A mercury thermometer reading (a) 20 °C and (b) 50 °C. The difference in the height of the mercury surface is the result of expansion of the liquid metal mercury, the bulk of which is in the bulb. Even though the expansion is relatively small, it makes a big difference to the height of mercury in the very fine tube attached to the bulb.

■ Does the volume increase or decrease when an ice cube melts? (Think about the winter time and the effect that the opposite process, freezing, can have on your car radiator or house water pipes.)

■ The volume *decreases* when ice melts.

The opposite effect is easier to demonstrate. If you freeze a bottle of water you are quite likely to crack the bottle as the ice forms and takes up a greater space than the original water. The increase in volume when water freezes means that ice is less dense than water. This explains why ice cubes float in your glass of iced water, and why icebergs float in the sea (Figure 6.16).

Water is very unusual in expanding on freezing, and we shall examine the reasons why this happens in Chapter 8, along with the explanation for the normal expansion of substances on heating and melting. However, all substances expand greatly on changing from a liquid to a gas. Taking water as an example once again, one litre of liquid water at its normal boiling temperature of 100 °C would become over one thousand litres of steam at atmospheric pressure when vaporized!

Gases also expand when heated, and to a greater extent than solids or liquids.

Figure 6.16
Icebergs near the Arctic Circle.

■ What might be difficult, do you think, about carrying out an experiment to see if a gas expands on heating?

■ Gases expand to occupy their container anyway.

So, if a gas is heated in a container with a fixed volume, the volume cannot increase; instead the *pressure* will increase. However, if it is arranged to keep the pressure constant (say at atmospheric pressure), then the volume of a gas does increase, and by a substantial amount. For example, heating air from a temperature of 20 °C to 300 °C will more than double its volume at atmospheric pressure.

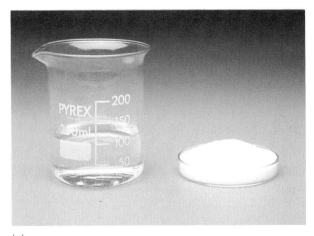

(a)

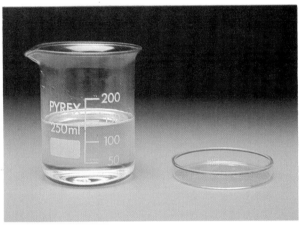

(b)

Figure 6.17
(a) Beaker containing 100 cm^3 of water, and a dish containing 50 g of sugar; (b) a solution of the sugar in the water.

6.4 Mixing and solution

One change of state that seems to confuse many people is the change that occurs when a solid is dissolved in a liquid. This has been referred to earlier in the discussion of hypotheses (Section 2.2). We say that we are making a solution of the solid in the liquid (Box 6.3). When you add sugar to water and stir, the sugar disappears and the solution looks just the same as it did to start with (Figure 6.17). This is *not* 'melting' the sugar in the water. It is *dissolving* the sugar in the water. The sugar has been dispersed evenly throughout the water, which is still a liquid.

▢ In the famous film *The Wizard of Oz*, when Dorothy throws water over the Wicked Witch of the West, the witch slowly turns into a puddle crying "I'm melting! I'm melting!" Is this likely to be correct?

▣ No. The effect of the water is almost certainly to cause the witch to dissolve, not to melt, which would require heating.

A solution is formed when one thing dissolves in another. A characteristic of solutions is that they are homogeneous. This means that there is only one state present, in this case the liquid state, and that there is only one *apparent* component, even at the biggest of magnifications. Solids are not the only things that can dissolve in liquids. In some cases, other liquids can dissolve in liquids, and gases can also dissolve in liquids.

▢ Can you think of any examples of liquids dissolved in liquids, and gases dissolved in liquids?

▣ Any bottle of wine provides a ready example of one liquid dissolved in another. The alcohol in the wine is a liquid and it is dissolved in the water that comprises most of the solution. Alcoholic liquors are not *the* solution but they are certainly *a* solution! Another alcoholic example illustrates the solubility of a gas in a liquid. A bottle of champagne with the cork still in place is a pale coloured homogeneous liquid, but when the bottle is opened the pressure is lowered and the dissolved carbon dioxide gas escapes in the familiar way.

It is not always the case that, when two things are mixed, a solution is formed. The two substances may retain their integrity such that they can be separated more or less readily into their individual constituents. They are insoluble and the result is simply a mixture in which each component is readily recognized. An example of this is a mixture of sand and water (a solid and a liquid) or of oil and water (two liquids) (Figure 6.18).

Box 6.3 Solubility of solids in liquids

When a solid dissolves in a liquid, we say it is soluble. What is produced is a **solution**. For example, a sugar solution is produced when sugar is dissolved in water. If you add enough sugar, then eventually no more will dissolve, and some solid will remain at the bottom of the container. This is then said to be a **saturated solution**.

You are probably also already familiar with the word **solvent** to describe a liquid that is used to dissolve something, like the water when making a sugar solution or the turpentine thinner ('turps') used to clean paint brushes. However, you may well not have come across the word **solute**, which is used for the substance that dissolves in the solvent.

Not all substances dissolve in a given solvent to the same extent. However much you try, you would find that you can only dissolve about 36 g of common salt (which has the chemical name sodium chloride) in 100 g of water at 20 °C. However, if you tried a related substance called sodium bromide, you would find that you could dissolve about 91 g in the same quantity of water at the same temperature. So sodium bromide is said to be more soluble in water than sodium chloride. Note the necessity to mention the solvent because it can happen that one substance is more soluble than another in one solvent but the order is reversed if you choose a different solvent.

Some substances, sand for example, dissolve in water to such a small extent that they are classed as being **insoluble**. However, as you saw from the dialogue earlier, to say that something is soluble or insoluble is not very scientific, because it is not specific enough. So generally, in talking about solubility, we describe substances using descriptions such as 'very soluble', 'moderately soluble', 'slightly soluble' or 'virtually insoluble'. In the last case, the qualifier 'virtually' is used because it is not possible to determine if a substance is actually insoluble or simply that the quantity that has dissolved is too small to measure.

There can also be a more complicated kind of mixing, in which a solution is not formed, but the product can appear at first sight to be homogeneous, in other words it appears to have a perfectly 'smooth' texture. A glass of milk looks homogeneous. It looks like a simple, white liquid but it is not. Milk is made up of fats suspended in water. The fats are not soluble in the water but are in the form of very tiny globules that are evenly dispersed throughout the water. (This is discussed in more detail in Book 3.) This kind of apparently homogeneous mixture is called a **colloid.** Colloids are mixtures that appear to be homogeneous, but are actually heterogeneous, in other words have a 'grainy' texture. A colloid does not necessarily need to be a liquid–liquid mixture. Smoke is a colloid and consists of solid particles suspended in a gas (the air); mist or fog is a colloid with a liquid (water) suspended in the air.

■ What do you think are the states of the components of the colloids, foam and jelly?

■ Foam is a gas suspended in a liquid (beaten egg white is an example), and jelly is a liquid (water) suspended in a solid matrix (gelatin).

A characteristic of all these colloids is that a sufficiently powerful microscope would reveal the presence of the different components showing that they are in fact heterogeneous mixtures, and not true solutions.

As with so much in science, we can learn about things using a simple model and then return to the same thing later using a better but more complex model. We shall return to solutions and mixtures when we have a model that lets us look at things in terms of their fundamental structures. But the time has come to consider what are the building blocks of which matter is made, before going on to examine how these determine the properties of matter.

Figure 6.18
A bottle of French salad dressing made of oil and vinegar, together with various herbs and seasonings. The vinegar is a *solution* of the substance acetic acid (a liquid) in water (another liquid); the oil and vinegar comprise a *mixture*, no matter how vigorously the bottle is shaken.

Summary of Chapter 6

Chemistry is concerned with matter. Matter can be defined as anything that has mass. An object with mass has a resistance to being moved, and is attracted to anything else with mass by the force of gravity.

Mass is defined in terms of a standard kilogram, a cylinder made of a mixture of platinum and iridium kept in Paris. Subsidiary standard masses are produced by comparison with the standard mass. These are then used to calibrate 'weights' for use with beam balances. Spring and electronic balances are also calibrated via these secondary standards in terms of the standard kilogram.

Though often confused, mass and weight are different properties. The confusion arises because the process of determining mass is termed 'weighing'. Weight is a measure of the force on an object due to gravitational attraction by the Earth, and so has units of force (newtons). Mass is the intrinsic property of the object and has units of kilograms or a sub-unit.

Matter takes on a number of forms and these are classified in terms of the solid, liquid and gaseous states. A solid has a shape independent of its container or environment; a liquid has a fixed volume, and a shape determined by the vessel containing it; a gas expands to fill its container, whatever its volume.

A force has to be applied to change the shape of a solid. Even if the solid is broken, the total volume and mass remain fixed. Some substances, such as fine powders like talc, do not seem to have all the properties of a solid; in particular, they take the shape of their container. However, at the microscopic level they are made of solid particles. Glass is an apparently solid material that also has properties akin to those of a liquid on a very long time-scale.

The change from one form to another, for example from solid to liquid or liquid to gas, is called a change of state. Changes of state of pure substances take place at a fixed temperature: at atmospheric pressure, these are called the normal melting temperature and the normal boiling temperature. The most common example is the melting of ice to give liquid water and the vaporization of water to give steam.

Solids and liquids expand to a small extent on heating, and melting is normally accompanied by an additional expansion. Ice, however, is an exception to this rule and contracts on melting. All substances, however, greatly expand on vaporization. Gases expand substantially on heating provided they are kept at constant pressure.

When a solid such as sugar is added to water it disappears. In this process the sugar dissolves in the water, it does not 'melt'. The resulting liquid is a solution of sugar in water. The water is called the solvent and the sugar is the solute. True solutions have a smooth texture even when examined with a very powerful microscope. Solutions can involve liquids or gases as the solute. Milk is an example of a colloid, which appears to be a solution but has a 'grainy' texture at high magnification. It is in fact a liquid–liquid mixture. Smoke and fog are also colloids, the former a solid–gas and the latter a liquid–gas mixture.

Question 17 Suppose that we took an electronic balance to the Moon together with a $50\,cm^3$ gold bar *without altering the calibration of the balance.* The force of gravity is only one-sixth as strong on the surface of the Moon as it is on the surface of the Earth. What do you think the reading on the balance would be when you tried to weigh the gold bar? (You can assume that this particular electronic balance can read to the nearest ten grams.)

Question 18 Explain, in terms of the pressures involved, why it is possible to push a drawing pin into a piece of wood with your thumb without experiencing much discomfort.

Question 19 Describe what you think takes place when you heat popcorn kernels in hot oil or a microwave oven to make them 'pop'. (Hint: even when dried, popcorn kernels contain some moisture.)

water vaporize
corn puffs up
as steam escapes

Question 20 In hot air balloons, a propane burner is periodically lit under the canopy of the balloon to heat the air. Explain why this enables the balloon to float in the air.

Chapter 7
A particular view of matter

7.1 A thought experiment

A device that is often used to stimulate research and to help to understand, or even define, a problem is the thought experiment. This is a rather fancy name for the kind of 'what if?' thoughts that we all have. Nevertheless, the thought experiment is very useful and is fun to do. (Or is it 'have'? Can you 'do' a thought? Can you 'have' an experiment?) Let's try a thought experiment to help us frame useful questions about the nature of matter. The question we wish to address just now is this: can we get to the ultimate structure of matter by continuously dividing a sample of a substance into ever smaller pieces? The thought experiment is to try to imagine what would happen if we did take something and keep dividing it into two pieces. At each stage we examine the newly divided sample and ask if it is the same substance as we started with.

Let's try this simple thought experiment with a piece of gold. Do we reach a point where we can no longer subdivide without losing the character that makes gold what it is? Or can we subdivide for ever? In other words, is there a particle that is the smallest possible thing that can still be called gold, or is there not? The first few divisions will be straightforward. There will just be less of the gold to see each time. As we continue dividing we will come to a time when the piece of gold becomes too small to see and we have to start speculating. Now what?

I think that we have to accept that there are (at least) two possibilities now. One is that there is no limit to the extent to which we can carry on dividing the gold without changing its nature. This is the hypothesis that matter is continuous. Another option is that eventually we reach a point where we can no longer subdivide without destroying the essential character, whatever that is, of gold. The logical conclusion in this case is that there is something, some entity, which is the smallest possible component of gold. If that entity is divided then you no longer have 'gold' but you have something else. That is the hypothesis that ultimately matter is composed of things called **atoms**.

- Do you think that one or other of these hypotheses can be refuted by pure reason – that is without doing any experiments?

- The very basis of the modern scientific method is that any hypothesis should be tested by experiment. Reason, unsupported by experimental evidence, is not sufficient to make scientific discoveries.

The early Greek philosophers, such as Plato and Aristotle, certainly did believe that the issue could be decided by reasoning alone. Although Plato believed that matter was made up of particles (see Box 7.1), Aristotle, his pupil, did not. He thought that matter was continuous. But experiments and observations have shown that the atomic model of matter is superior in almost every respect. It allows us to rationalize and predict chemical behaviour in a way that the continuous model does not.

Box 7.1 The early Greek philosophers and the atomic theory

The suggestion that matter is composed of particles that could not be further divided originated with Leucippus and his follower Democritus around the 5th century BC. Democritus (born about 460 BC) combined his belief in the four earthly elements with the theory that elements were composed of collections of indivisible, fundamental particles that he called 'atoms'. Each of the four elements had atoms of a different shape.

Plato also believed that elements were composed of particles whose shape affected their properties. Plato was an accomplished mathematician and this influenced his view of the Universe. The series of three-dimensional shapes in which each face is a regular figure, identical in shape and size to every other face, is called the Platonic solids. He thought that the atoms of the elements would have one of these shapes (Figure 7.1).

Plato thought that the particles that made up earth were cubes, because they stack together very well so that earth has strength and solidity. Water is less dense and less packed than earth and it flows, so it was logical that Plato chose for water particles the more spherical icosahedron, with its twenty triangular faces. The particle for fire had to be one that could get everywhere and penetrate matter. He chose the sharp, four-faced tetrahedron for the fire particle. Air was an octahedron. Things that were not pure earth, air, fire or water were composed of different proportions of the different shaped particles.

These shaped particles are purely the result of philosophical

Figure 7.1
The shapes of the four elements according to Plato: (from the left) fire; earth; water; air.

consideration. It is, however, interesting to know that the idea that the shape of the ultimate particle does influence the behaviour of the bulk material is one that we use in modern science. It is an idea that you will meet quite soon.

Aristotle thought that matter must be infinitely divisible. In other words any piece of an element, no matter how tiny, would still have all the characteristics of that element. That idea predominated over the atomic theory until the beginning of the 19th century, when John Dalton (see next Section) showed unequivocally that each chemical element must be composed of atoms characteristic of that element. However, the physical nature of atoms remained controversial for many years. In fact, it was not until the early years of the 20th century that this was clarified, and a unification between the chemical and physical views of atoms was finally achieved.

7.2 Atoms

We are now so accustomed to the idea of atoms that you may well have read some of the previous pages with impatience. Everyone has heard of atom bombs and atomic power, even if they are not sure quite what these terms mean. But the existence of atoms is not obvious. It took more than 2 000 years for the idea to become accepted. In fact, there was still strong opposition to the idea even at the turn of the 20th century – probably during your great grandparents' or even grandparents' lifetime!

By the 18th century there was significant support for a model of the structure of matter involving some kind of particle. The ideas about earth, air, fire and water being the fundamental substances, the elements, were largely discredited. There was still a great deal of confusion in chemistry and there were many hundreds of unexplained observations. Through experimentation, a lot was known about chemical change or the changing of one substance into another. By thinking about the experiments and classifying reactions in a number of ways, it seemed that there probably were elements, but not of the type the Greeks wrote about. As we saw in Chapter 3, it was Boyle and Lavoisier who developed definitions of the chemical elements that are close to the modern one.

The definition evolved that an **element** was something built up from fundamental particles, unique to that element, that can be neither created nor further subdivided by chemical change. That is still a reasonable working definition. The gigantic problem of how you could tell what was an element and what was not, dominated the lives of numerous scientists for many years.

John Dalton (Figure 7.2), a schoolteacher in the Lake District and Manchester for much of his life, was the first to put forward a systematic atomic theory of matter in his book *A New System of Chemical Philosophy* published in 1808. In it he proposed that elements were composed of atoms. Substances that were not elements were compounds, in which the fundamental particle was a combination of atoms. The beauty of this was that chemical combination could now be understood within a logical framework.

There were many aspects to his theories but the main ideas that he put forward still survive today (although some are now modified or qualified in some way). One of the most important was that *every element has its own unique type of atom*. Each atom was also said to have a definite mass, which Dalton stated was the same for every atom of that element. Atoms of different elements have different masses.

Although Dalton thought that you could never discover the actual mass of an atom, he was able to determine the *relative* masses of different atoms. He discovered that the element hydrogen has the lightest atoms, so he used the mass of a hydrogen atom as the standard for his scale of **relative atomic masses**. Dalton's measurements indicated that the oxygen atom had seven times the mass of the hydrogen atom, so on Dalton's scale the relative atomic mass of oxygen was 7.

Although many of Dalton's relative atomic masses were quite wrong (the relative atomic mass of an oxygen atom is 16.0, not 7), that was unimportant, at the time, by comparison with the advance in understanding chemical behaviour that resulted from the atomic theory (see Box 7.2). Not everyone was convinced, though, even as late as the 1880s. The eminent English chemist Sir Henry Roscoe commented in 1887: 'Atoms are round bits of wood invented by Mr. Dalton.' However, the predominant view was that Dalton's atomic theory finally provided the necessary framework for the systematization of chemical knowledge and paved the way for modern chemistry. This was the certainly the belief of the famous German chemist

Figure 7.2
John Dalton (1766–1844). Born in Cumberland, Dalton was a Quaker who spent most of his life as a tutor at Manchester New College. It was his interest in meteorology that first caused him to consider atoms as the fundamental particles of matter. Dalton also investigated colour blindness as he was himself colour blind (in fact, colour blindness is sometimes known as Daltonism). You will learn more about the causes of colour blindness in Book 4.

1803–1873

Justus von Liebig, who wrote in 1854:

> *All our ideas are so interwoven with the Daltonian theory, that we cannot transpose ourselves into the time when it did not exist... Chemistry received in the atomic theory, a fundamental view; which overruled and governed all other theoretical views. ... In this lies the extraordinary service which this theory rendered to science, viz.: that it supplied a fertile soil for further advancements: a soil which was previously wanting.*
>
> *(Quoted in W. H. Brock,* The Fontana History of Chemistry, *Fontana Press, 1992, p. 171)*

Dalton laid the foundations of modern chemistry with the atomic theory. Almost all of chemistry is now related to properties of atoms and combinations of atoms. We shall now look more closely at current models of the atom. The gold 'thought experiment' in Section 7.1 is a useful starting point. We shall start the experiment with a piece of gold that is a cube with each side measuring one centimetre in length. Now we cut the gold in half, take one half and cut that in half. Let us assume for our thought experiment that after each cut we zoom in so that by the time we have made three cuts, the resulting cube looks to the eye to be the same size as the original (Figure 7.4).

Box 7.2 Dalton's atoms and chemical change

Dalton invented his own symbols for the elements (Figure 7.3), and he used them to express chemical change.

Water was known to be formed when hydrogen was burned in oxygen. There was no available way at the time to determine how many atoms of each element combined to give water. So, as an initial hypothesis, Dalton assumed that they combined in the simplest possible combination, which is one of each. He expressed the reaction between the two elements in the form of a chemical equation. The reaction between hydrogen and oxygen was written as follows:

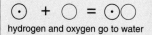

hydrogen and oxygen go to water

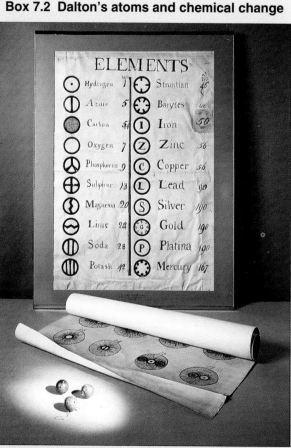

This was a forerunner of the modern chemical equation, which is a cornerstone of the language of chemistry. We don't use Dalton's symbols any more, but instead use simple alphabetical symbols, such as O for oxygen and H for hydrogen, to represent elements (and their atoms).

Figure 7.3
Dalton's symbols for substances that he thought were elements. The substances magnesia, lime, soda, potash, strontian and barytes have since been shown to be compounds.

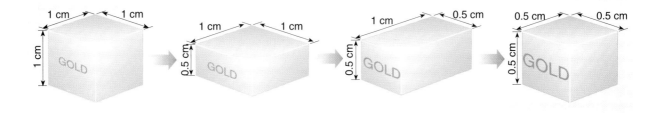

Figure 7.4
The thought experiment of progressively cutting a cube of gold into half, then half again, and so on, each time zooming in so that the resulting cube-shaped piece of gold after three cuts seems to be the same size as the original.

After about 64 divisions or so the gold will take on a distinctly grainy look as about two thousand or so particles make up the block (Figure 7.5, first picture). If you look at these particles very closely, you will see that they are perfectly spherical; furthermore, they are not jumbled together but are arranged in a regular way. Such an arrangement is called a **crystal lattice**.

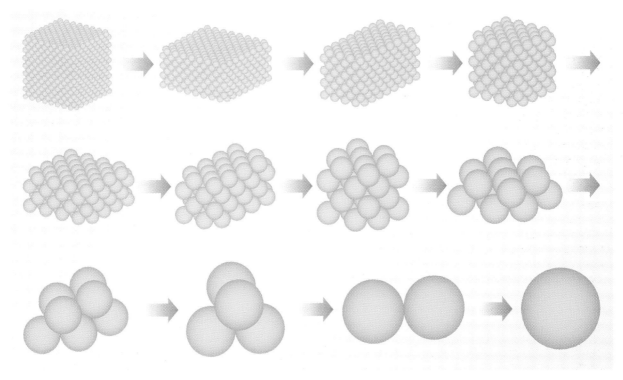

Figure 7.5
The last eleven divisions in the thought experiment. The first picture (top left) shows the gold remaining after about 64 divisions.

After about 11 more cuts (that is about 75 or 76 in total) we would finally be left with one single gold atom (Figure 7.5). That spherical atom is the fundamental building block of the element gold.

That gold atom is unique to gold. It is comparatively very massive and has a relative atomic mass of 197 on Dalton's scale. On our scale of things it is very tiny indeed, and we can never see an atom with the naked eye or even with the best optical microscope. Until recently, scientists wishing to visualize atoms and the way they are arranged had to rely on indirect evidence. However, a new technique called scanning tunnelling microscopy has enabled images to be obtained that are the nearest we have to a picture of an atom. Figure 7.6a shows such a picture of a layer of gold atoms; for comparison, Figure 7.6b shows a model of such a layer produced by a computer graphics package, and Figure 7.6c shows the relationship of the layer to the arrangement of gold atoms shown in Figure 7.5. You will learn more about scanning tunnelling microscopy and the amazing images that it is capable of producing in Book 4.

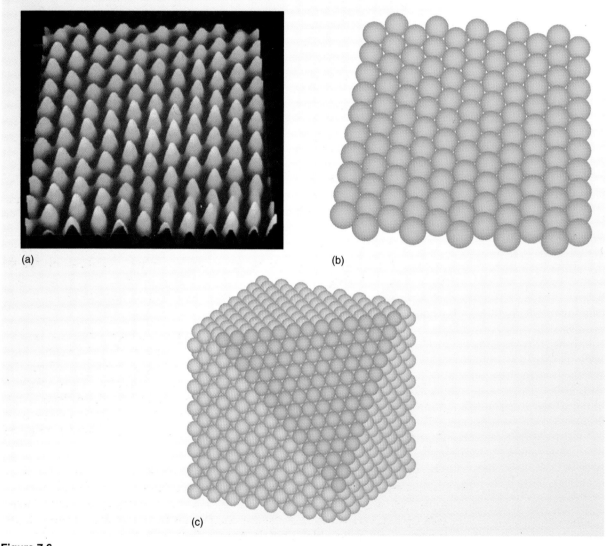

(a)

(b)

(c)

Figure 7.6
(a) An image of a layer of closely packed gold atoms on the surface of a crystal obtained by scanning tunnelling microscopy; (b) a computer-generated model of a layer of gold atoms as in (a); (c) the relationship of such a layer of gold atoms to the atomic lattice shown in the first picture in Figure 7.5.

In just 75 divisions starting with our original 1 cm^3 cube, we have gone right away from any scale that belongs to our experience. (To get an idea of how fast things change when you double or halve progressively, work out how much money you would have if you had been given £1 at birth which was then invested in a scheme that guaranteed to double your money every year. You would have been a millionaire by the time you reached your 21st birthday!) One of the problems facing the early chemists was that chemistry happens at such a small scale. If we want to understand chemical reactivity in terms of 'this thing reacts with that thing' then we have to relate to that tiny scale. It really isn't surprising that some people believed that matter was continuous, because it *looks* as if it is!

The mass of a gold atom is 0.000 000 000 000 000 000 000 33 g (3.3×10^{-22} g) and its diameter is about 0.000 000 000 3 m (3×10^{-10} m or 300 pm). Because of the problems with so many zeros in real atomic masses, we still use the concept of relative atomic mass. However, rather than basing it on hydrogen being 1 as suggested by Dalton, we now define it rather differently, as we shall see shortly in Box 7.3. We also use alphabetical representations for the elements and their atoms, rather than Dalton's symbols. For example, hydrogen is H, oxygen is O and gold is Au, from *aurum*, which is the Latin word for gold. You will learn more about the symbols used for other elements and about their relative atomic masses a little later on.

7.3 The structure of the atom

We now know that atoms are not indivisible, and this means that we need to refine our model of the atom. Nuclear energy derives from the splitting of atoms into smaller components, and nuclear physicists have discovered an entire menagerie of particles from which matter is composed. Of those there are only three that directly concern chemists. The spherical gold atom that we came to in our thought experiment is electrically neutral, as are all atoms. As we shall see, this is not the case for at least some of the particles of which atoms are composed.

If you have light fly-away hair (unless it has flown away already), you can make it literally stand on end by rubbing it vigorously with an inflated balloon, and then holding the balloon a few centimetres above your head. In a similar vein, if two balloons with strings attached are rubbed on your hair and then you hold them by the strings and attempt to bring them close together you will find that they repel each other. Although these may seem like trivial party tricks they do tell us something important about the structure of the atom.

In ancient Greece, where there was so much curiosity about nature, it had been noticed as early as 600 BC that a piece of amber, when rubbed vigorously with animal fur, acquired the property of being able to attract and pick up feathers. A modern phenomenon that is related to these observations is particularly noticeable in hotels. As you walk along the corridor to your room your feet rub against the carpet. When you reach your room, you take the key from your bag or your pocket and move it towards the inevitable metal door handle. If the conditions are just right, then you see a spark that can be several centimetres long pass between you and the door, and at the same time you feel a sharp pain in your hand.

These are all related phenomena and you might know them as 'static electricity'. The rather random nature of these experiments was systematized starting in the 18th century by Benjamin Franklin (Figure 7.7), famous for his experiments involving lightning. It was Franklin who coined the terms positive and negative charges, and defined them as follows:

- **negative charge** is the type of charge similar to that produced on amber, or hard rubber, by stroking it with fur;
- **positive charge** is the type of charge similar to that produced on glass by stroking it with silk.

It was already known that charged amber rods repelled one another and that charged glass rods also repelled one another. However, when a charged amber rod was touched to a charged glass rod, they both lost their charges. Franklin explained these observations by suggesting that like charges repel. He also found that unlike charges attract one another.

The materials start off being electrically neutral, which is the usual state for matter. The rubbing process separates electrical charges in the materials. When the amber rod is rubbed, negative charges are transferred from the fur to the rod. The opposite is true for glass rubbed with silk: in this case, the negative charge accumulates on the silk leaving the glass positively charged.

There are within any atom equal numbers of positively charged particles and negatively charged particles. The charge on each particle is one fundamental charge unit, either positive or negative. The negatively charged particles are called **electrons** (after the Greek word for amber, ελεκτρον (elektron)) and the positively charged particles are called **protons**. All atoms except for hydrogen also carry a certain amount of 'ballast' in the form of a third type of particle called **neutrons**, which bear no charge but do have mass. *One element is distinguished from another only by the number of protons each atom contains (which, of course, equals the number of electrons).* The number of protons in the atom is called the **atomic number** (Box 7.3). Of the 109 elements known 94 are found in nature, of which ten occur in only trace amounts. All matter is built from this extremely small set of building bricks. During the Course you will see how such a small 'atomic Lego' set is used to construct the almost infinite variety of our world.

It was discovered around 1910 that although the *charges* of a proton and an electron are equal and opposite, their *masses* are very different. Protons are massive compared with electrons: an electron has only about 1/2 000th (actually 1/1 836) of the mass of a proton. A neutron has almost exactly the same mass as a proton. So you can assume to a good approximation that the relative atomic mass of any given atom can be calculated simply by counting the number of protons and neutrons it contains. For example, carbon-12 has six protons and six neutrons.

■   There are 79 electrons in an atom of gold-197. How many protons and neutrons are there?

■   The total number of protons and neutrons in the atom is approximately equal to the relative atomic mass, that is 197. In calculating the relative atomic mass we can ignore the mass of the electrons and concentrate on the number of protons and neutrons. We also know that, as an atom is electrically neutral, the numbers of protons and electrons must be the

Figure 7.7
Benjamin Franklin (1706–1790). The most important American scientist of his period, Franklin was also one of the foremost statesmen of the American Revolution and one of the signatories of the Declaration of Independence.

(handwritten annotations:)

So (79) electrons + (118) neutrons + (79) protons

protons + neutrons = 197

79 electrons mean
79 protons

x neutrons + 79 protons = 197

∴ number neutrons = 197 − 79
= 118

Box 7.3 Isotopes

Atoms of a particular element all have the same number of *protons*. However, it is possible for different atoms of one element to contain different numbers of *neutrons*. Atoms that differ only in the numbers of neutrons they contain are called **isotopes** of the element in question. For example, most hydrogen atoms contain just one proton and one electron; they have no neutrons. This type of hydrogen atom is given the symbol H. But there are hydrogen atoms that contain one proton, one electron and one neutron. These are still hydrogen atoms, because the identity of an element is determined by the number of protons, not the number of neutrons. The hydrogen isotope with relative atomic mass 2 is one of the very few that have been given their own name and symbol. It is called a **deuterium** atom, symbol D (from the Greek word δευτεροσ (deuteros) meaning second). Water containing deuterium atoms instead of hydrogen atoms is often called 'heavy water'.

All elements exist as at least two isotopes; for example, there are three isotopes of carbon. The most common type of carbon atom has six protons and six neutrons, a total of 12 particles in the nucleus, so it is called carbon-12. A second type of carbon atom has six protons and seven neutrons, so is called carbon-13; it occurs naturally to the extent of about 1%. The third type, which has six protons and eight neutrons, is called carbon-14. Carbon-14 is unstable and radioactive. Because these all have six protons, they are all carbon atoms and they all have the same atomic number.

The modern scale for relative atomic mass is based on the mass of carbon-12 being exactly 12. On this scale, the relative atomic mass of hydrogen is 1.01, not 1.

You may have come across the term isotope in a number of contexts. Isotopes are used in medical studies as tracers to investigate the biological processes going on in the body; they are used in the testing of new drugs before they are made available to the general public; and they are used for archaeological dating – the most familiar being carbon-14. However, chemistry is dominated by protons and electrons and, in general, we shall not be concerned with isotopes of elements unless there is a particular reason.

---

same. If there are 79 electrons then there must be 79 protons in a gold atom. The remainder of the 197 atomic mass units must be from neutrons, so there are 197 − 79 = 118 neutrons in a gold atom. So the structure of the gold atom can be considered to be 79 protons + 79 electrons + 118 neutrons.

Finally in this first look at atomic structure, we can ask the question 'How are these protons, neutrons and electrons arranged in the atom?' One of the first guesses at an answer to that question was put forward in 1898 by J. J. Thomson (1856–1940), famous for his researches into the nature of the electron. He proposed that an atom might look something like a round Chelsea bun or a plum pudding, with the pastry being the main part made up of protons and neutrons, and the electrons being like currants dispersed throughout the 'pudding' (Figure 7.8). This was a tasteful model of the atom but it did not survive after 1910.

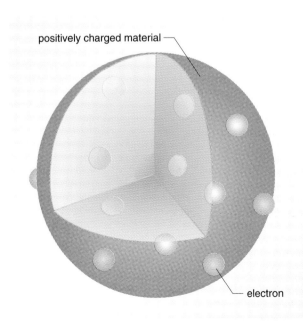

positively charged material

electron

Figure 7.8
The Thomson 'plum pudding' model of the atom, with negatively charged electrons (blue) embedded in positively charged material (red).

Gold has featured very strongly in the history of chemistry and it was an experiment with gold that helped to show the structure of an atom. Gold can be beaten into very thin sheets (known as gold leaf) less than 0.000 1 mm (10^{-4} mm) thick. Gold leaf is extremely light: a square metre weighs only about 1.6 g. Because it is so thin, despite the very high value of gold, it is economic to use gold leaf for decoration, such as gold inlays in rare books, particularly mediaeval ones, and even for covering the domes of some churches, such as many in Russia (Figure 7.9).

You have almost certainly read something about radioactivity. Certain isotopes of some elements are unstable, they self-destruct. As they do so, the atoms break down into smaller atoms, and smaller particles and/or radiation are often emitted. One type of emitted particle is called an alpha-particle: these are made up of two protons and two neutrons, and so are positively charged. Radium, an element discovered and investigated by Marie Curie (1867–1934), breaks down spontaneously and ejects alpha-particles. Marie Curie was awarded the Nobel Prize for Chemistry in 1911 for her work on radium.

One of the great scientists of the 20th century, Ernest Rutherford (1871–1937), saw in alpha-particles an opportunity to probe the structure of the atom. With his assistants Geiger (of Geiger counter fame) and Marsden, he devised a clever experiment. They directed a stream of alpha-particles at a piece of gold leaf. They then observed the way in which the alpha-particles were scattered after passing through the gold leaf, by means of flashes produced when the particles struck a movable fluorescent screen (Figure 7.10). By watching for the flashes, Rutherford was able to determine the number of alpha-particles scattered at various angles from the gold leaf.

Hans Geiger 1882–1945

Ernest Marsden

Figure 7.9
The golden domes of a Russian Orthodox church within the walls of the Kremlin in Moscow.

First of all, Rutherford and his colleagues observed the flashes produced by the beam of alpha-particles directly, without the gold leaf being in place. Perhaps not surprisingly, the flashes they observed fell in a small circle no bigger than the size of the beam. Then the gold leaf was put in position.

They expected the beam to be scattered by the gold atoms. Instead, they made the surprising observation that most of the flashes occurred in the same position as before, at the centre of the screen. It was almost as though the gold leaf just wasn't there!

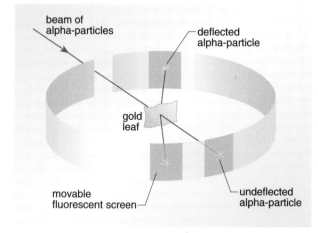

- What does the fact that most of the alpha-particles pass straight through the gold leaf without any deflection tell you about the structure of the atom?

- The atom must consist mainly of empty space, otherwise most of the alpha-particles would be scattered.

Figure 7.10
Rutherford's gold foil experiment. To avoid scattering of the alpha-particles by the air, the whole apparatus had to be placed in an evacuated chamber.

The second surprising observation was that some flashes were seen right at the edge of the screen, so Rutherford and his co-workers moved the screen round in a circle to try to find the maximum deflection produced. To their

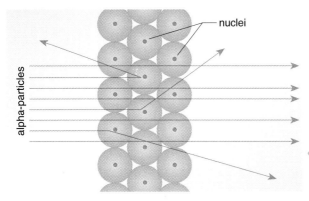

Figure 7.11
The scattering of alpha-particles in Rutherford's gold foil experiment.

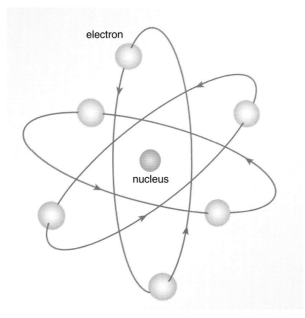

Figure 7.12
The Rutherford model of the atom. Gold atoms have many more protons and electrons than are shown here.

great surprise, they found some flashes that corresponded to some of the alpha-particles (around 1 in 8 000) that did not pass through the gold but bounced back in the direction from which they came (Figure 7.11).

Clearly, this was not compatible with the plum pudding model of the atom, in which matter is evenly distributed! Rutherford later described the observation of the reflected alpha-particles 'as if you had fired a 15-inch shell [a very large naval artillery shell fired from the battleships of the day] at a piece of tissue paper and it came back and hit you.'

■ What does the fact that a few of the alpha-particles bounce back tell you about the structure of the atom?

■ The atom must have a very small but massive component which occasionally an alpha-particle hits head-on.

From these observations Rutherford gained the clues to put forward a new model for the structure of the atom (Figure 7.12). He proposed that the atom is constructed of a very dense core of protons and neutrons, called the **nucleus**. In the nucleus there are protons packed very closely together. They are all positively charged and so repel each other, but we now know that, when they are as close together as they are in a nucleus, a very short range force – a sort of atomic superglue – holds the nucleus together. Compared with the overall size of the atom the nucleus is very tiny. As we saw earlier, the gold atom has a diameter of about 3×10^{-10} m (300 pm). However, the nucleus is much smaller: Rutherford was able to calculate that it is about 1/10 000 of the diameter of an atom, or of the order of 10^{-14} m (0.01 pm). Rutherford suggested that the electrons orbited the nucleus, rather like a miniature planetary system. Although the electrons repel one another, this is overcome by the attraction between the electrons and the positively charged nucleus.

So the mass of an atom is concentrated at the centre in a very small volume. When the alpha-particles are fired at the gold leaf, what the alpha-particle experiences, or would see (if it could see) would be a regular array of hard massive (in mass not size) dots that take up only a small amount of the space through which it is travelling. There is only a very small chance (1 in 8 000) that the alpha-particle will meet the nucleus head-on and rebound back to its origin. Rutherford's hypothesis about the structure of the atom formed the basis of modern atomic theory, although now there are more direct ways of showing that atoms have 'hard' centres and 'soft' outsides.

Rutherford's model of the atom has the attraction of simplicity and certainly explained the results obtained from the scattering of alpha-particles. However, it soon became necessary to refine this model. It turns out that electrons cannot be adequately described as particles similar to billiard balls or marbles. We usually say that they have a dual nature. In some circumstances they behave like charged particles, but at other times they behave like a wave. In describing the behaviour of electrons in atoms, we normally talk about the electron(s) as forming a 'cloud' around the nucleus (Figure 7.13). The cloud shows the probability of finding an electron at a given point, with the region where the cloud is most dense representing where the electrons spend most time.

We shall not dwell further on the nature of electrons as they are not simple to model using examples that we can easily understand. We shall just use whichever model is appropriate to the discussion.

In the discussion of the experiments involving the rubbing of amber or glass rods, you may have noticed that we took care to say that the rods either gained or lost *negative* charge, rather than say that they gained or lost *positive* charge. That was because the electrons in an atom have greater mobility than the protons: they can be moved around more readily than their massive nuclear counterparts. Electricity is the flow of electrons in a circuit. And at its most fundamental, much of chemistry is about the way in which electrons move from atom to atom, and the way in which electrons are distributed in a substance.

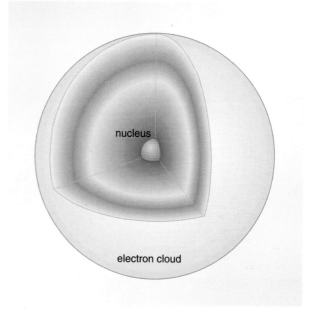

Figure 7.13
The modern model of the atom.

Now that we have a good working model of the atom, we can start to look at the nature of substances that are made up in some cases from the atoms of a single element, and in others from combinations of atoms of different elements. It is at this stage that we start our intellectual journey exploring the structure of things around us. Although there are some difficult things to grasp, it is possible to understand the basis of the shapes and structures of natural and unnatural things by applying a relatively small set of ideas and models. The structure of matter depends on the ways in which atoms combine to form larger building blocks that stick to each other and to other types of particle, that combine, repel and generally behave with a fascination that increases with every new thing you discover.

7.4 Molecules

Here is another thought experiment. Take a drop of water, and divide it the 70 or so times needed to see what a water particle looks like. What would you see? There is actually quite a lot to this question, but first we shall concentrate on the smallest portion of water that can have an independent existence. As the number of cuts increases, the 'graininess' of the material called water becomes apparent. But there is a distinct difference between water and gold. With gold the building block, the atom, was spherical and uniform. Water is built up not from spheres but from particles constructed from three atoms joined together in a fixed way. This collection of atoms is called a **molecule**. The word 'molecule' is a general term for a group of atoms that are joined together in fixed proportions with a particular geometric arrangement around each atom. The water molecule is made up of one oxygen atom with two hydrogen atoms bonded to it.

It is important to note that the atoms in a molecule are joined together. They are held together by **chemical bonds**. What is the nature of a chemical bond? Consider again the structure of an atom. It has a positively charged, small nucleus surrounded by a cloud of negative charge. Negative and positive charges attract each other, so the electrons stay around the nucleus. Two atoms when brought together will initially repel each other because the electrons both have the same type of charge: they are both negatively charged, and like charges repel. But when two atoms are brought very close together so that the two electron clouds surrounding the nuclei can overlap, they mix to form a sort of electron cloud surrounding both atoms (Figure 7.14).

With the two nuclei surrounded by an electron cloud that encompasses both of them, there will be a distance where the repulsion between the two positively charged nuclei is exactly balanced by the attraction between the electrons and the nuclei. This type of bonding, in which electrons are shared between two nuclei, is called **covalent bonding**. The distance between the two nuclei that are bonded together is called the **bond length** (Figure 7.14). In each water molecule, for example, the distance between the centre of the oxygen atom and each hydrogen atom centre is about 0.000 000 000 1 m (10^{-10} m or 100 pm). This very small distance is the same for all oxygen–hydrogen separations in water molecules.

Because we cannot 'see' atoms directly in the way that we can see a Lego set, it is not really meaningful to ask what the water molecule looks like. But of course we do ask, because we always want to relate things to our own experience. We need to be able to visualize them in order to understand how they behave. So we build a bridge between what we think these sub-microscopic entities are like and what we do know about. In other words we make models. But remember, models are necessarily simplified versions of the real thing. So that we may use the most appropriate model in trying to get an answer to what the water molecule would look like, we need to define more closely what features of the molecule we are particularly interested in.

The structure of an atom was said to be a hard dense core surrounded by a cloud of electrons. Are we going to 'see' the electrons or just the nuclei? In some circumstances, the best view of a molecule would be the one in which all the space that it occupies is seen, in other words a model that represents the electron cloud. This is the type of model that we used to depict gold atoms in Section 7.2. In other instances, we might be more interested in the way in which the nuclei in the molecule are arranged relative to each other. So, no single 'view' of a molecule gives all the information that might be needed at one time or another. To overcome this, several different ways of visualizing molecules have been developed. Some, like the gold atoms we have seen, involve the use of computer-drawn images; others involve the use of physical model kits.

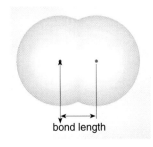

Figure 7.14
Schematic diagram of a covalently bonded molecule made up of two identical atoms, showing the bond length.

pm = picometre
= 10^{-12} m.

Covalent – linking atoms by a bond in which pair of electrons is shared.

It is not possible to go very far in chemistry without some means of constructing molecular models. Indeed, it was only by constructing a model of the DNA molecule that Watson and Crick were able successfully to decipher the genetic code. Increasingly, chemists are making use of computer programs that allow the construction of molecular models as images on a screen (Figure 7.15). But for many chemists, one of the essential tools of the trade is still a molecular model kit. It is a remarkable thing that models of all the substances in the world could be built using an atomic set of only one hundred or so different types of component. Of course many, many millions of each piece would be needed!

Figure 7.15
Molecular modelling by computer.

There are different types of model kit. Some are designed for seeing how a molecule occupies space (Figure 7.16a). These are called space-filling models and show the space occupied by the electrons. There are also kits designed simply to show the geometry of molecules. These are called framework models (Figure 7.16b). Some kits are made very accurately, like a scale model kit for making cars or aeroplanes, so that the relative distances between the centres of the atoms relate to the actual distances in a real molecule.

The kit you will be using in this Course, called the Molymod kit, shares features both of the framework and the space-filling models. It is called a ball-and-stick model, and it shows the relative geometry of molecules while representing the atoms as spheres (Figure 7.16c). These spheres are smaller than the full 'space-filling' size so that the interior of larger molecules can be seen more clearly.

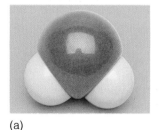

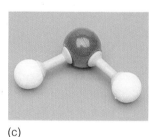

(a)   (b)   (c)

Figure 7.16
Models of a water molecule made using (a) a space-filling model kit, (b) a framework model kit, (c) the ball-and-stick model kit used in the Course.

You will be asked to make some models using the Molymod kit shortly. You will then get more practice in using this kit as you progress through the Course. However, in Book 1 we shall use mainly computer-generated models. These use representations that mirror the three types of physical model. Computer-modelling has a number of advantages over using a model kit. One is that larger models are not subject to the laws of gravity, and so don't fall apart so easily! A second is that it is much easier with a computer to make sure that the models are drawn precisely to scale. In general, we shall use ball-and-stick and/or space-filling representations.

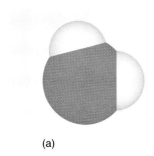

(a)

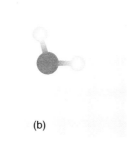

(b)

Figure 7.17
Computer-drawn models of a water molecule: (a) space-filling model; (b) ball-and-stick model.

In Figure 7.17, the water molecule is shown in two different ways. The first (Figure 7.17a) is a space-filling view. Note that the central oxygen atom is larger than the hydrogen atoms. This is reasonable, as hydrogen has just one electron whereas oxygen has eight, and hence its electron cloud is that much larger. The second view (Figure 7.17b) is a ball-and-stick model. This enables the relative positions of the centres of the atoms in the water molecule to be seen more easily. It also accurately represents the geometry of the molecule in a visible way. The angle between one of the oxygen–hydrogen bonds and the other is about 104 degrees (104°) in every water molecule. This is called the **bond angle**.

The 'bent' nature of the water molecule is an essential part of the molecular structure of water, and helps to determine the structure of liquid water and ice. The fixed geometric relationships in molecules are what ultimately gives everything its form and structure. Without fixed geometric relationships in molecules most of our world would collapse into a structureless heap. We shall explore this in more detail very soon.

So a molecule of water consists of two hydrogen atoms and one oxygen atom. Using symbols, we can write this as H_2O, and we call this the **chemical formula** of water (you may recall that Dalton thought that the chemical formula for water was HO (Section 7.2)). In writing a chemical formula, the number of each type of atom in the molecule is indicated by a subscript after the symbol for the element. So for water, the formula H_2O means that there are two hydrogen atoms and one oxygen atom in each molecule (the subscript '1' is assumed if no other number is written). This formula for water is the first formula in the Course, and water is the first chemical compound that we have discussed in detail. Notice that the formula H_2O is used to represent both a single water molecule and also water as a compound (Box 7.4). A substance made up of a large number of molecules of the same kind is called a **chemical compound** when the molecules are made up from atoms of more than one element. Water, far from being one of four elements as thought by the Greeks and later scientists, is a chemical compound.

The mass of a molecule is the sum of the masses of its constituent atoms. Hence the **relative molecular mass** of a molecule is simply equal to the relative atomic masses of all the component atoms added together.

Box 7.4 The three 'worlds' of chemistry

One of the reasons why many people have difficulty with chemistry is because chemists simultaneously work on three different levels and often switch from one to the other without saying so! The first of these is the macroscopic 'world': this is the level that deals with descriptive chemistry, with the observations that chemists make when, for example, a beaker of water boils. Nowadays, chemists have very powerful instruments that can measure minute amounts of material and provide essential data for a wide variety of purposes. But even if only a nanogram (10^{-9} g) or even a picogram (10^{-12} g) is involved, this is still the macroscopic world.

As you have just discovered, matter is thought to be made up of atoms and molecules, and chemists interpret observations at the macroscopic level in terms of the behaviour of atoms and molecules. This then is the second 'world', the scale we have so far described by the term 'sub-microscopic' and which, for convenience, we shall refer to from now on as the molecular level, even though it encompasses atoms and ions as well as molecules.

The third 'world' is the symbolic level and it connects the other two. This is when chemists use formulas such as H_2O to represent water. The confusing aspect is that H_2O sometimes can mean a molecule of water, and it can sometimes mean a beaker full of water! Which is meant at any particular time should be obvious from the context, and in this Course we shall endeavour to make it clear which level we are working on at any instant. However, we may forget and anyway, you may wish to read other books where the authors have been less explicit about which world they are talking about, so it is just as well to be aware of the three 'worlds' of chemistry.

One final point concerning nomenclature as it relates particularly to water: in future, if we simply use the word water, we mean either liquid water or the chemical compound water in whatever physical state it happens to be. Which meaning is correct should be clear from the context. If we wish to talk about the three states of water (the compound), we shall refer either to ice, water and steam or possibly solid water, liquid water and gaseous water. Because of the ubiquitous nature of water, confusion can occur if you are not aware of the different meanings possible for the one name.

■ Calculate the relative molecular mass of a water molecule. (Take the relative atomic mass of oxygen, O, to be 16 and that of hydrogen, H, to be 1).

■ Since the relative molecular mass is simply the sum of the relative masses of all the atoms in a molecule, for water, H_2O, it is $(2 \times 1) + (1 \times 16) = 18$.

Even in Dalton's time it was known that water was formed when hydrogen gas was burned in air. Air contains oxygen, and it is the reaction of hydrogen with oxygen that forms water. When anything that contains hydrogen in its molecules is burned in air, water is produced.

■ What does that tell you about wood (think back to your observations with the burning match)?

■ When the match was burned, water was produced, so wood must contain hydrogen atoms somewhere in its molecular structure.

The oxygen in the air is present not as O atoms, but as *molecules* of oxygen, in which two oxygen atoms are joined together. The chemical formula of oxygen is thus O_2. Oxygen is an element, but this illustrates that elements can exist as molecules. Many elements do exist in molecular rather than atomic forms. Hydrogen is also an element, and usually exists as molecules in which two hydrogen atoms are joined by a covalent bond. The chemical formula of hydrogen is thus H_2.

7.5 What's so special about carbon?

If you use natural gas for your cooking or heating you are using the chemical compound methane as the fuel. Methane is the simplest of a class of compounds that comprises more than 90% of all known compounds. These are the **organic** compounds, and their common feature is that they all contain carbon atoms, and in most cases the carbon atoms are bonded to other carbon atoms, often with other atoms and usually hydrogen as well. Carbon is an element and is the subject of a later Chapter in this Book. Suffice it to say here that carbon is unique in its ability to form bonds between its own atoms in chains essentially without limit. It is for this reason that so many different carbon compounds are possible. As you will learn later in the Course, this property is the key to the creation of plastics, to the chemistry involved in nutrition and health, and in the manufacture of many of the dyes that we use to brighten our surroundings.

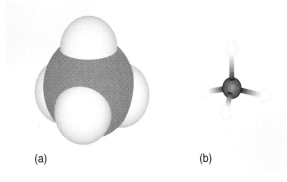

(a)   (b)

Figure 7.18
(a) Space-filling model of a methane molecule;
(b) ball-and-stick model of a methane molecule.

Natural gas consists predominantly of molecules of methane (it also contains something to make it smell, as methane itself is odourless). Each methane molecule contains one carbon atom and four hydrogen atoms, so the chemical formula for methane is CH_4. The ball-and-stick and space-filling models of the molecule are shown in Figure 7.18. When using symbols, the 'sticks' representing bonds in the ball-and-stick models are denoted using a line; for example, the bond between a carbon atom and a hydrogen atom is denoted as C—H.

The methane molecule is perfectly regular in shape. Every one of the H—C—H bond angles is 109°, and every one of the bond lengths is 109 pm. The shape of the methane molecule is described as a regular tetrahedron, as the hydrogen atoms are at the vertices (corners) of the Platonic solid tetrahedron and the carbon atom is at the centre (Box 7.5).

four sided — triangular pyramid

■   How many chemical bonds are there in methane?

■   There are four bonds in methane. Each hydrogen atom has one bond to the central carbon atom. The carbon atom has all four bonds attached to it.

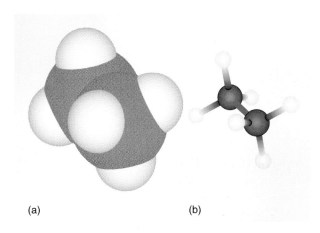

Methane is the simplest member of a group of compounds that contain only hydrogen atoms and carbon atoms and are called **hydrocarbons**. The next simplest hydrocarbon is ethane. Ethane has the chemical formula C_2H_6 and, like methane, is a gas at room temperature and normal atmospheric pressure. Two models of an ethane molecule are shown in Figure 7.19.

Figure 7.19
(a) Space-filling model of an ethane molecule; (b) ball-and-stick model of an ethane molecule.

(a)   (b)

Platonic solid — one of five regular solids
Plato

Box 7.5 Chemistry in three dimensions

In talking about constructing molecular models, we said that computer-based modelling had some advantages over the use of model kits. One advantage that physical models have over computer-generated pictures is that they are three-dimensional (3D). However, computer-generated 2D pictures do have a 3D effect incorporated and one of the skills that you will acquire during the Course is to be able to look at pictures of molecular models and imagine them in 3D. Indeed, later on we shall depict molecules using more abstract representations, and you will find that you slowly acquire the ability to visualize the geometry of molecules from such

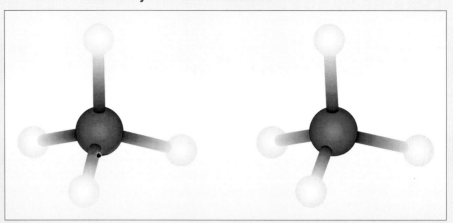

Figure 7.20
Stereoscopic ball-and-stick model of methane.

structural formulas.

However, from time to time, you will need to be able to look at 2D structures and see them in 3D in order to fully understand particular points to be made. To allow this, we shall make use of what are called stereoscopic pairs, such

as shown in Figure 7.20. This is a stereoscopic pair of a model of the methane molecule. To see the 3D effect, you will need to get the 3D spectacles that you have been sent and put them together according to the instructions supplied. Placing the spectacles on the page

centred over the stereo images and allowing your eyes to relax should allow you to see the image in 3D. Do not be concerned if it takes a few seconds for your eyes to adjust, particularly the first time. On future occasions the 3D effect will be easier to perceive.

■   Look at the ball-and-stick model of ethane. How many bonds are there to each carbon and how many to each hydrogen?

■   There are four bonds to each carbon and one to each hydrogen. These are the same numbers as there are in the methane molecule.

If you compare the models of methane and ethane, you will see that ethane has one type of bond that methane doesn't have. This is a bond between two carbon atoms. This is unimaginatively, but simply, called a carbon–carbon bond, and is represented as C—C. The structure of ethane gives you the first clue about some of the 'rules' governing the construction of molecular models: hydrogen atoms always have one bond to them, and carbon atoms always have four bonds to them.

Figure 7.21
Hydrogen (H) and tetrahedral carbon (C) atomic centres from the model kit.

Our model kit has 'hydrogen atoms' that allow only one bond to be made to them and 'carbon atoms' that allow four bonds to be made, with the characteristic tetrahedral geometry (Figure 7.21).

Activity 10 Building hydrocarbon molecules

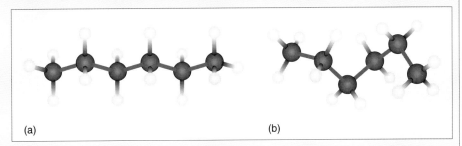

(a)   (b)

Figure 7.22
(a) Ball-and-stick model of hexane; (b) ball-and-stick model of hexane twisted into a different shape or 'conformation'. These represent molecules of the same compound, just as photographs of a person standing up and sitting down are not different people, but different 'shapes' of the same individual.

For this activity you will need to use your Molymod model kit. For further information about the kit, consult the Course Study Guide.

Hexane, another hydrocarbon, has the chemical formula C_6H_{14}. However, this does not tell us how the atoms are joined together. In fact, hexane has the six carbon atoms all joined in a row. The carbon atoms at each end are joined to three hydrogen atoms and one carbon, whereas the four middle carbon atoms are each joined to two other carbons and two hydrogen atoms.

With six carbon centres and 14 hydrogen centres you can build a model of a molecule of hexane. Try to construct such a model. You will need to use the shorter of the two types of grey plastic connector. Start by making CH_2 units from one carbon atomic centre and two hydrogen atomic centres: you should make six. Then join these CH_2 units together and add the final two hydrogen atoms, one at each end. Your finished model may look like one of the ones in Figure 7.22 or it might not.

You will find when you make the model that it is flexible. But if you look carefully at the model while moving it around, you will find that the bond lengths and the various bond angles do not change. Rotation about the carbon–carbon bonds is easy in the model and easy in the real molecule. (By rotation about a bond we mean that the part of the molecule at one end of the bond rotates relative to the rest of the molecule at the other end of the bond (Figure 7.23).) Very precise information about the way that molecules undergo these internal flexings is available to the modern chemist.

(continued overleaf)

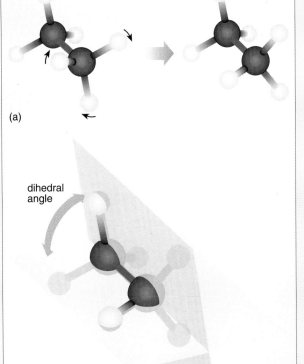

(a)

dihedral angle

(b)

Figure 7.23
(a) A bond rotation in an ethane molecule. Notice that the bond angles do not change, that is the angles between two C–H bonds or between a C–H bond and a C–C bond. What does change is the so-called dihedral angle as shown in (b). (b) The dihedral angle is the angle between two planes, for example one defined by the two carbon atoms and a hydrogen attached to the nearer carbon atom, and the other defined by the two carbon atoms and a hydrogen attached to the farther carbon atom.

The fact that hexane molecules can, and do, change their shape very easily does not affect the compound hexane. A worm wriggling around is still a worm whether it is straight, bent or curled. There is only one compound with the formula C_6H_{14} and with six atoms of carbon joined in a row, and that is hexane.

There are thousands of ways in which tetrahedral carbon atoms and hydrogen atoms can be combined together. Take another six carbon centres and join them together randomly without attaching any hydrogens. See how many different arrangements you can find in ten minutes. Then compare yours with those shown in Figure 7.24. Beware of finding too many! Check with your models that your carbon frameworks really are different and not just the same thing looked at from a different angle. Another possibility is that two might look quite different but be joined together in the same way and you have two different flexible forms.

All the arrangements in Figure 7.24, when the

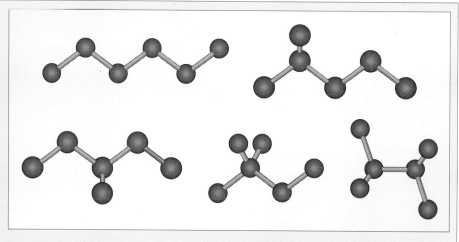

Figure 7.24
The different ways that six carbon atoms can be connected together.

hydrogen atoms are added, have the same formula, C_6H_{14}. They are models of the different possible molecules with that formula and they are all different compounds with different names (Box 7.6). So now we have reached a point where the chemical formula of a compound is not sufficient by itself to specify exactly what a compound is. If you were working in a laboratory and were asked to go and get some C_6H_{14} you would have the choice of several compounds. But if you were told to get hexane you would only have one choice. Different compounds with the same chemical formula are called **isomers.**

When you were joining your six carbon atoms together, you may have joined them so that one end of a chain joined the other end to make a ring. If so, you may have wondered why they were not included in the structures above. In those structures we only included chains, not rings.

■ Take your six carbon atoms and 14 hydrogens. Join the carbon atoms in a single ring containing all six atoms. Add the hydrogen atoms onto the appropriate places on the carbon atoms. What happens?

■ There are two hydrogen atoms left over!

It would be possible to make models using the six carbon atoms which had five carbon atoms in a ring, or four, or even, with a bit of strain, three. In each case you would find you only need twelve hydrogen atoms to fill the remaining holes. All the compounds with six carbon atoms that contain one ring have the formula C_6H_{12}.

All the compounds of carbon that have been discussed so far follow the simple rules that each carbon has four bonds to it and each hydrogen has one bond to it. The bond lengths are all about the same for each type of bond. A C—H bond is about 109 pm long and a C—C bond is about 154 pm. The bond angles are all about 109°.

Box 7.6 What's in a name?

A few years ago, I was on a visit to the USA with my family. My elder daughter developed a temperature. She is allergic to aspirin, and unfortunately we had neglected to bring any paracetamol with us. No problem, I thought, we can get some from the nearest drug store. Unfortunately, there didn't seem to be any, and the shop assistants had not heard of paracetamol. So I began to look more carefully along the shelves where the analgesics were displayed and spotted a well-known product called Tylenol®.

The packet informed me that the Tylenol tablets contained something called acetaminophen. This is where my chemistry background came in, because I soon realized that this was simply paracetamol by another name, a conclusion that I quickly confirmed by looking in a dictionary of drugs (US drug stores stock an amazing variety of items, including books!).

Neither paracetamol nor acetaminophen is the full chemical name for the analgesic: that is *para*-acetylaminophenol. To a chemist, that name is unambiguous, but as you can see, it is less convenient and 'user-friendly' than the two abbreviated forms. (You can readily see how these were coined: paracetamol from ***para*-acet**ylamin**ol**, and acetaminophen from *para*-**acet**yl**aminophen**ol.)

Inevitably, during the Course you will meet quite a large number of chemical names, and sometimes more than one name for the same compound, often a brief one used industrially and by the general public (sometimes called the *trivial* name), together with the 'proper' (or *systematic*) chemical name. Just as the various views of a molecule (e.g. space-filling and ball-and-stick) have different uses, the same is true of trivial and systematic names.

Be reassured, however, that **you do not have to commit any of these names to memory**. We shall always give the name, whether in the text, an audiovisual sequence, an assignment or an examination question, whenever it is needed, and you will never be expected to work out the name of a compound for yourself. Just as with people, names will in general be used simply for identification; anything further will be explained whenever necessary.

Does this mean that all ten million or more known compounds containing carbon, including most of the molecules that you and I are made of, have only the one carbon building block, with four bonds and tetrahedral geometry? Well no, there are actually four different carbon building blocks, each with its own particular properties. The simple organic compound ethene (formerly called ethylene) has the formula C_2H_4; ethene is the starting material for making polyethene (sometimes called polyethylene or polythene). Ethane has the formula C_2H_6, so is the formula for ethene two hydrogens short of a molecule? The answer is no, it follows perfectly the rule that carbon has four bonds to it by having *two* carbon–carbon bonds between the two carbon atoms. This is called a **double bond** and is represented as C=C. The ball-and-stick model of an ethene molecule and the space-filling model are shown in Figure 7.25.

polyethene
= polythene
= polyethylene

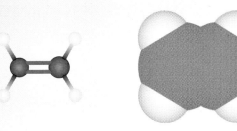

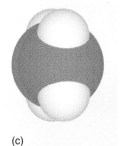

Figure 7.25
(a) A ball-and-stick model of ethene; (b) a space-filling model of ethene viewed face-on; (c) the same model as in (b) but viewed end-on.

(a)   (b)   (c)

Count the bonds to each carbon in the ball-and-stick model in Figure 7.25. Notice that there are two bonds between the carbon atoms rather than the one that you have seen so far. So there are still four bonds to each carbon and one to each hydrogen. The most striking difference between the molecular structure of ethane, C_2H_6, and ethene, C_2H_4, is that ethene is a flat molecule. The bond angles at a double-bonded carbon are 120°, and in the ethene molecule all six atoms are in the same plane, as shown by the space-filling model. In contrast to the carbon–carbon single bonds, double bonds are stiff and rotation about them does not normally occur. The geometry about a double bond is fixed, so ethene is not a flexible molecule, as you will find out shortly when you build a model.

There are four carbon building blocks and two have been covered so far. One has four single bonds to it and bond angles of about 109°, and the other has two single bonds and one double bond to it and bond angles of 120°.

■   Can you think what other combination there could be at a carbon atom using the types of bond that you have met already?

■   The carbon atom could maintain four bonds to itself by having two double bonds.

This is the third possibility, and compounds with two double bonds to one carbon atom are known. Carbon dioxide, CO_2, which was produced along with water when you lit the match, is a colourless and odourless gas, and it has two double bonds to a carbon. In this case they are carbon–oxygen double bonds, represented as C=O, and they are allowed because oxygen always has two bonds to it (remember, in the water molecule oxygen is attached to two hydrogens). Models of carbon dioxide are shown in Figure 7.26. The three atoms are in a straight line in the molecule, which is described with characteristic clarity as being linear.

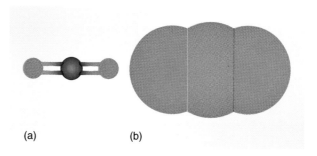

(a)   (b)

Figure 7.26
(a) Ball-and-stick and
(b) space-filling models of a
carbon dioxide molecule.

■   What does that make the bond angles in carbon dioxide?

■   The bond angles are 180°.

This particular building block occurs in rather few compounds, however, and the only example you will meet is the carbon dioxide molecule.

There is only one carbon building block left to describe and that is the bonding found in ethyne (formerly called acetylene) and related compounds. Ethyne, which has the formula C_2H_2, can be made easily by pouring water onto the substance calcium carbide, CaC_2. This chemical reaction was used in the early 1900s in car and bicycle lamps (Figure 7.27). Water was dripped steadily onto the solid calcium carbide, and ethyne was produced. This reaction takes place with the production of heat, and this heat is sufficient to ignite the ethyne, which burns with a bright flame.

Figure 7.27
Acetylene bicycle lamps with canisters of calcium carbide.

The bonding between the two carbon atoms in ethyne is described as being a triple bond, because there are three bonds between them, represented as C≡C. This leaves one bond on each carbon for bonding to hydrogen. The models of this molecule are shown in Figure 7.28. Note that the bond angles are 180° and that the molecule is rather rod-like.

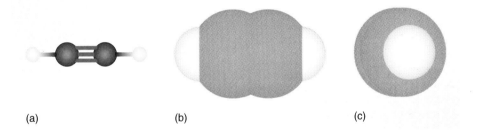

Figure 7.28
(a) A ball-and-stick model of ethyne; (b) a space-filling model of ethyne viewed side-on; (c) the same model as in (b) but viewed end-on.

(a)   (b)   (c)

Many substances that we come across in our everyday lives are made of molecules. With the atomic centres shown in Figure 7.29 (Box 7.7, overleaf) we are in a position to make models of a wide range of such molecules. However, there is another whole group of substances that are made of a quite different type of building block, which we shall meet in the next Section.

C_2H_6 C_2H_4 C_2H_2

Activity 11 Ethane, ethene and ethyne

For this activity you will need six carbon centres and 12 hydrogen centres. You will also need 13 short connectors and five of the longer flexible connectors.

First, build a model of the ethane molecule (formula C_2H_6) as follows: join two carbon centres using a short connector; then attach hydrogens to the remaining six holes, also using short connectors.

Second, build a model of the ethene molecule (formula C_2H_4) as follows: attach two of the flexible connectors to a single carbon centre, then attach the loose ends to a second carbon centre; then attach hydrogens to the remaining four holes, using short connectors.

Finally, build a model of the ethyne molecule (formula C_2H_2) as follows: attach three of the flexible connectors to a single carbon centre, then attach the loose ends to a second carbon centre; then attach hydrogens to the remaining two holes, using short connectors.

Compare the three models, and identify the main differences between them.

When you have done this, remember to look at the Comments on Activities at the end of the book.

$a \rightarrow e \rightarrow y$
C_2H_6 C_2H_4 C_2H_2

Box 7.7 An atomic 'Lego' set

There are literally millions of molecules we could examine: there are more than twelve million with a known structure! Fortunately, it is not necessary to look individually at hundreds of molecules to understand chemical structure. The idea of an atomic Lego set with its hundred or so different building blocks, together with a few simple rules, is enough to be able to understand, or even more impressively, to predict the structures of molecules. In this Course we shall concentrate on just a small subset of these.

Most molecules that we shall meet during the Course contain a relatively small number of different atoms. In Figure 7.29 we show twelve of the most frequently occurring types of atomic centre. With this limited set of building blocks, you should be able to construct most of the molecules we shall be interested in.

Note that, as is apparent from Figure 7.29, we use a generally accepted colour code to be able to identify the more common atom types easily: carbon is black (Molymod kit) or dark grey (computer-drawn image); hydrogen is white; oxygen is red; nitrogen is blue; and so on.

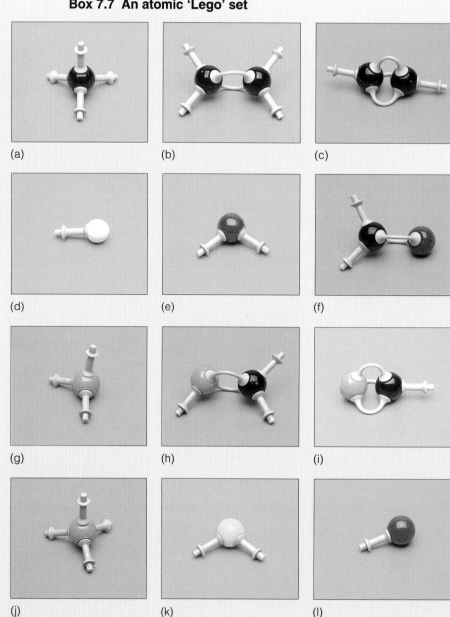

(a)   (b)   (c)

(d)   (e)   (f)

(g)   (h)   (i)

(j)   (k)   (l)

Figure 7.29
Twelve of the most frequently occurring atomic 'building blocks': (a) carbon with four single bonds; (b) carbon with two single bonds and a double bond (attached to another such carbon); (c) carbon with one single bond and one triple bond (attached to another such carbon); (d) hydrogen; (e) oxygen with two single bonds; (f) oxygen with one double bond (attached to a carbon); (g) nitrogen with three single bonds; (h) nitrogen with a single bond and a double bond (attached to a carbon); (i) nitrogen with one triple bond (attached to a carbon); (j) nitrogen with four single bonds (the nitrogen in this case carries a single positive charge – see later in the Course); (k) sulfur with two single bonds; (l) fluorine, chlorine, bromine or iodine (these elements are collectively called the halogens and are represented in our model kit using the same coloured centre).

7.6 Ions and crystals

Covalent bonds, the electron-sharing bonds that bind together molecules such as ethane and water, are not the only way that chemical compounds can be held together. Other substances have structures that depend for their properties on the attraction of opposite electric charges.

One of the most startling demonstrations of the power and effects of chemical change is the reaction between the metallic, shiny element sodium, Na (Figure 7.30a), and the toxic, pale-green, gaseous element, chlorine, Cl_2 (Figure 7.30b). They react together almost explosively (Figure 7.30c) to form the white, water-soluble solid called sodium chloride, which is best known as common salt (Figure 7.30d). Salt is, of course, eaten in substantial quantities by all of us (even by those on a low-salt diet). This dramatic change in colours, tastes and other properties occurs during the reaction because *each sodium atom transfers one electron to a chlorine atom.*

Figure 7.30
(a) Sodium metal (immersed in oil to prevent reaction with oxygen and moisture in the air); (b) chlorine gas; (c) the reaction between sodium and chlorine; (d) sodium chloride (common salt).

(a)

(b)

(c)

(d)

- A sodium atom in sodium metal has 11 protons in its nucleus, which is surrounded by 11 electrons. If the sodium atom loses an electron how many protons and electrons are left, and what is the overall electrical charge?

- There are 10 electrons left, and the number of protons stays unchanged at 11. The overall charge on what is left is therefore +1.

The entity that remains after electrons are lost (or gained) from atoms is called an **ion**. An ion is an atom (or it can be a group of atoms) that carries an electrical charge. Positively charged ions are called **cations** (pronounced 'cat-eye-ons') and negatively charged ions are called **anions** (pronounced 'ann-eye-ons'). The sodium cation is written Na^+, in which the superscript 'plus' sign indicates one positive charge on the ion. A superscript 'minus' sign is used for anions.

How would you write the anion derived from chlorine, in which each chlorine atom gains one electron? (Note that the anion from chlor*ine* is called chlor*ide*.)

By analogy with the sodium ion the way to write the chloride anion is Cl⁻, in which the superscript minus sign indicates one negative charge.

We shall consider the reasons for sodium losing an electron and chlorine gaining one in Chapter 9. For now, let's return to common salt and its structure. Unlike metals, which form structures that do not break easily, salt is quite crumbly, and some people use a salt mill to grind coarse salt into finer pieces for food flavouring.

You see common salt probably every day. What can you say about its form?

It is definitely granular. If you look closely at the grains you may be able to see that many of them are cubic in shape. In other words, they have all six sides the same size with all of the angles between the edges being perfect right angles (90°).

Salt can form only cubic grains. Those grains that are not cubic are most likely broken pieces or several cubes joined together. These grains are called **crystals**. Crystals can come in a huge variety of shapes and sizes (Figure 7.31). It is possible to make a salt crystal grow bigger, by putting it in a solution containing a lot of dissolved salt and allowing the water to evaporate slowly. Slowly, more sodium chloride crystallizes out of the solution and attaches itself to the initial crystal. When this happens, the enlarged crystal stays exactly the same shape. This process can also occur naturally (Figure 7.32). The shape of a crystal is characteristic of the particular substance from which it is made, and derives from the internal order within that crystal.

Figure 7.31
Crystals of calcite (left), quartz (centre rear), iron pyrites (centre front), and amethyst (right).

Figure 7.32 (right)
A large crystal of naturally occurring sodium chloride.

Sodium chloride crystals are made up of a regular array of positively charged sodium ions and negatively charged chloride anions (Figure 7.33). Just as with gold atoms, this array of ions is called a crystal lattice. The crystal lattice is held together by the attraction between the oppositely charged ions: because of the arrangement of the ions, this attraction is greater than the repulsion between ions with like charge. Even in the smallest crystal there are untold millions of ions present. But whatever the size of the crystal, it has no overall charge because the number of negative charges is always exactly balanced by the number of positive charges.

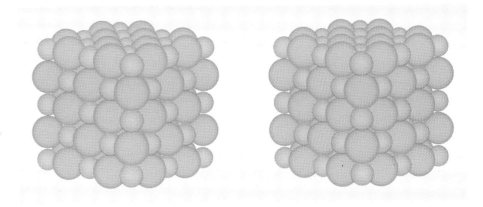

Figure 7.33
Stereoscopic model of the sodium chloride crystal. The ions are shown in their space-filling representation. The sodium ions are grey and the chloride ions are green.

In the crystal, each sodium ion is surrounded by six chloride ions, each of which is exactly the same distance away from the sodium ion as the other five (Figure 7.34). The same is also true for the chloride anions, which are surrounded by six sodium ions (Figure 7.35). This is a very efficient way to pack the oppositely charged ions. It is much more efficient than having the ions randomly distributed. When you pack a suitcase you can get much more in it by packing it carefully than by just throwing everything into it at random.

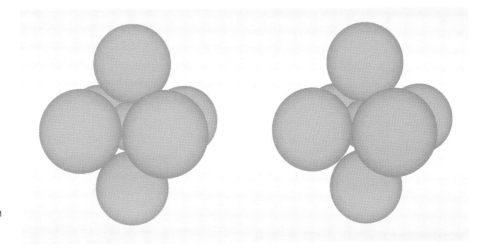

Figure 7.34
Stereoscopic model of a sodium (Na^+) ion in a sodium chloride crystal with the cation surrounded by six chloride anions.

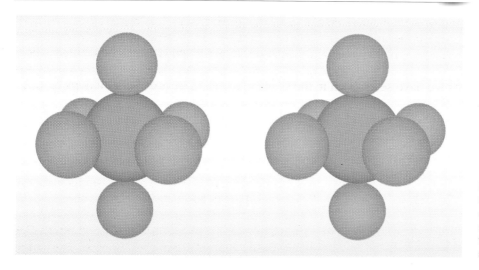

Figure 7.35
Stereoscopic model of the chloride (Cl⁻) ion in a sodium chloride crystal with the anion surrounded by six sodium cations.

The question arises, how do we represent the formula of sodium chloride? With molecules, it is relatively straightforward to count up the number of each type of atom. But in a crystal of an ionic solid *there are no molecules*. There is just a very large array of ions arranged in a particular way. The way round this problem is to represent the formula of an ionic solid as the smallest number of each type of ion that gives a correct indication of the composition of the solid. For sodium chloride this means that, since there are equal numbers of sodium ions and chloride ions in the crystal, we write the formula as NaCl, rather than Na_2Cl_2 or Na_3Cl_3, and so on. In writing the formula as NaCl, we are using a form of shorthand: it is not meant to indicate that there are NaCl molecules – as we have said, there are no molecules in an ionic crystal; second, the charges are taken for granted, in this case the single positive charge on each sodium ion, Na^+, and the single negative charge on each chloride ion, Cl^-.

Crystals are efficiently and regularly packed 'suitcases' of ions (or molecules or atoms)! At the moment we are considering a crystal made up of oppositely charged ions, but crystals can be made up of more or less any type of chemical entity: Figure 7.36 shows an example of a **molecular crystal**; gold is an example of a crystal made from atoms (Figure 7.5). The defining characteristic of a crystal is that the building blocks are stacked in a regular and repeated way. The way in which the components of a crystal are packed is usually the most efficient way of packing those components into a regular pattern.

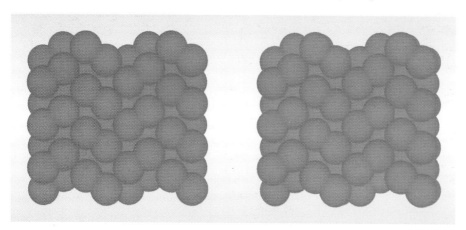

Figure 7.36
A stereoscopic model of a crystal of the element iodine. Iodine exists in the form of I_2 molecules. A space-filling representation is used to emphasize the way the molecules pack together.

Covalent
— linking atoms by
a bond in
which pair
electrons is
shared

When we considered the way in which atoms were connected together by covalent bonds to form molecules, it wasn't very difficult to specify that arrangement because of the limited number of atoms in the molecule. Specifying the arrangement of ions in a crystal is a little more difficult because, as we have seen, even in the smallest crystal there are many millions of ions.

▨ Can you see how we could go about specifying the arrangement of ions in a crystal in a relatively simple way?

◼ The key is to look for a repeat unit.

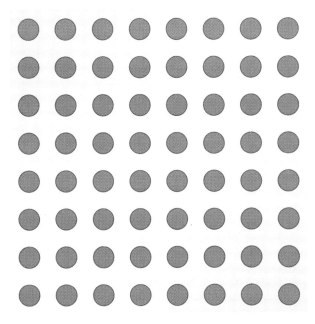

Suppose we wanted to specify an arrangement of particles that are laid out on a sheet (more scientifically described as being in a **plane**). A regular pattern in two dimensions is shown in Figure 7.37. What would be the repeat unit for this pattern?

As a first try, you might say that, because all the dots are the same, the repeat unit is simply one dot. However, this is insufficient.

▨ Why do you think one dot is insufficient as a repeat unit?

◼ It contains no information as to the distance apart of the dots.

Another attempt at specifying the repeat unit might be that shown in Figure 7.38a. While this is an improvement on the first attempt, it is still not quite right as you can see in Figure 7.38b, which is an array made up of the repeat units shown in (a).

Figure 7.37
Regular array of particles lying in a plane, e.g. as at the surface of a crystal lattice.

The correct repeat unit does not have a whole circle, or atom, at each corner but a *quarter* of a circle or atom (Figure 7.39a). So, when the units fit together in a plane there is exactly one circle at each point where four repeat units meet. This is like a tile with a pattern on it, such as you might use in a kitchen or bathroom (Figure 7.39b).

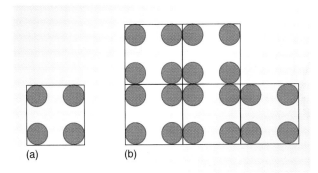

(a)   (b)

Figure 7.38
(a) An attempt at identifying the repeat unit of the array in Figure 7.37; (b) an array made up of the repeat units shown in (a).

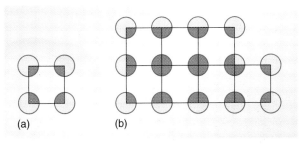

(a)   (b)

Figure 7.39
(a) The exact repeat unit of the array in Figure 7.37 as defined by the area within the square showing the quarter circles (atoms) in blue; (b) the 'tiling' of repeat units to give a fragment of the array shown in Figure 7.37 – the blue circles or part-circles are on the 'tiles', the green part-circles show the segments that would be provided by additional 'tiles'.

When we think about real crystals we have to transfer our thoughts into three dimensions. The repeat unit has to be rather like a small suitcase or small packing-case packed with exactly the right arrangement of atoms (or parts of atoms) in the right places to define the structure for as big a crystal as we want to make. That tiny suitcase, repeated enough times could make a crystal as large as or larger than the dome of St Paul's Cathedral if you had enough material.

This defining arrangement for a crystal, this 'packing case', is called a **unit cell.** The unit cell for sodium chloride is shown in Figure 7.40. It happens that the unit cell for sodium chloride has a cubic shape: crystals of other substances can have other shapes. It is the sizes of the different groups or atoms, their types and their charges that determine the exact size and shape of the unit cell. Unit cells will be discussed at greater length in Book 2.

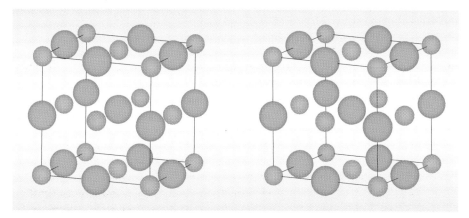

Figure 7.40
A stereoscopic model of the sodium chloride (NaCl) unit cell. The unit cell is the volume enclosed by the lines in black. Note that in drawing unit cells, we don't attempt to draw half, quarter or eighth atoms, but remember that such atoms are shared by more than one unit cell. The ions have been reduced to 25% of the space-filling size for clarity.

Ionic solids are generally crystalline at room temperature. One of the reasons for this is that the forces that attract oppositely charged ions to one another extend over significantly greater distances than the forces between individual molecules. Water, for example, has molecules that consist of two hydrogen atoms bound in a fixed geometric relationship to a central oxygen atom. Each molecule of water is surrounded by others, but the forces between the molecules are very weak compared with the forces holding the atoms together within each molecule. Therefore it is relatively easy for water molecules to slip and slide around each other. We shall return to this later when we discuss the differences at the atomic and molecular level between solids, liquids and gases.

You may have wondered what determines the distances by which ions are separated in crystals. That is quite complicated, but you can perhaps get some understanding of why, say, sodium and chloride ions are separated by a particular distance. The opposite charges will attract the two ions and that attraction increases as the ions get closer. In opposition to that is the fact that ions are not infinitely compressible.

If you have two beach balls and you press them together (that is equivalent to an attractive force) the two balls will be compressed until you reach a point where you can no longer compress them with the force that you are applying. You have reached a point of equilibrium where the force pushing the two balls together is balanced by the resistance of the balls to being compressed.

The same is more or less true with ions. An equilibrium distance apart is reached where the attractive force between nearest neighbours is exactly balanced by the repulsive force between the electron clouds of the two adjacent ions. Now you may be able to see why a crystal is a stable thing with a defined shape. If you try to move an ion in any direction you will have to force it, and there will be an opposing force trying to restore the ion to its equilibrium position.

To summarize, a crystal made up of ions has a very regular, repeating pattern. The non-directionality of the attractive forces between ions allows the ions to be packed in the most efficient way possible, which produces the beautiful variety of crystalline forms that are known.

The only ionic crystal that we have looked at is the relatively simple sodium chloride crystal, which is made up of sodium cations, Na^+, and chloride anions, Cl^-. Ions do not necessarily consist of only one atom. Ions can resemble molecules in having a collection of atoms fixed together in a fixed geometry by covalent bonds, with the only difference between them and a simple molecule being that the ion bears one or more charges. You will learn more about ions and crystals in Book 2.

Summary of Chapter 7

Consideration of the structure of matter leads to two possibilities: either matter is continuous and can be subdivided without limit, or it is made of a fundamental building block, a unit the early Greek philosophers termed the atom. Plato believed in the existence of atoms and proposed that the atoms of the four elements should have particular shapes. Though these were pure invention, the idea that the shape of the ultimate particle affects the behaviour of matter is still in use. However, Aristotle's idea that matter was continuous predominated until the 19th century.

Dalton was the first to put forward a systematic atomic theory of matter. He proposed that elements were composed of atoms. Substances that were not elements were chemical compounds in which the fundamental particle was a combination of different atoms. Dalton stated that every element has its own unique type of atom with a definite mass, which was the same for every atom of that element.

Atoms of different elements have different masses. Dalton based his scale on hydrogen having a relative atomic mass of 1. He also invented his own symbols for the elements and used them to represent chemical reactions. Dalton's pictorial symbols for the elements have been replaced by an alphabetical representation.

By rubbing two materials together, such as amber with fur or glass with silk, the amber or glass acquires the property of attracting light materials such as hair or feathers. This is the phenomenon of static electricity, and it arises because the rubbing induces electrons to transfer from one material to another. Experiments showed that amber and glass acquire charges of opposite properties. Benjamin Franklin proposed that amber acquires negative charge and that glass acquires positive charge.

Atoms are not indivisible. They are composed of protons, which are positively charged, neutrons, which have zero charge, and electrons, which are negatively charged. Electrons are about 1/2 000 of the mass of a proton. One element is distinguished from another by the number of protons each atom contains. The number of protons in an atom is called the atomic number. Atoms with a different number of neutrons but the same number of protons are called isotopes. The modern scale of relative atomic masses is based on the carbon-12 isotope being given a value of 12.

One model of the atom was proposed by Thomson and resembled a plum pudding, with negatively charged electrons embedded in a larger particle with positive charge. Rutherford's experiments, in which alpha-particles were fired at gold leaf, showed this to be incorrect: most of the mass of an atom is concentrated in a very small nucleus containing the protons and neutrons; the much lighter electrons surround the nucleus. In the modern model of the atom, the electrons form a cloud around the nucleus.

Many chemical compounds (and some elements) exist in the form of molecules. A molecule is a group of atoms that are joined together in fixed proportions with a particular geometric arrangement around each atom. The atoms in molecules are held together by chemical bonds in which electrons are shared between the two atoms at either end of the bond. This is called covalent bonding. The distance between the nuclei of two bonded atoms is called the bond length; the angle between two bonds is called the bond angle.

Molecules are modelled using both model kits and computer-generated images. Each has advantages and disadvantages. There are three main types of model, whether made from a kit or drawn by computer: framework, showing just the positions of the nuclei; space-filling, showing the space occupied by the electrons; and ball-and-stick, where the sizes of the atoms are some fraction of the full space-filling size. Colour coding is used to distinguish the atoms of different elements.

Because of the unique ability of carbon atoms to bond to each other, the vast majority of compounds known contain carbon. As the number of linked carbon atoms grows, the number of ways in which they can be connected together increases. So molecules can have the same chemical formula, but different structures: such compounds are called isomers. In addition to linear structures, carbon compounds can contain one or more rings of atoms. Compounds can also have double bonds (as in ethene and carbon dioxide) or triple bonds (as in ethyne).

Covalent bonds are not the only way that chemical compounds can be held together. Other substances have structures that involve the attraction of particles with opposite charges. These particles are called ions and are atoms that have lost one or more electrons (such as the sodium cation: that is, a positively charged ion) and atoms that have gained one or more electrons (such as the chloride anion: that is, a negatively charged ion). Ions form regular arrays called crystals, which are held together by the attractive forces between oppositely charged ions. These attractive forces exceed the repulsions between ions of like charge. Crystals can be any size, and so the structure of a crystal is specified in terms of the unit cell, the smallest unit that faithfully represents the crystal lattice.

Question 21 As discussed in the text, gold can be beaten into very thin gold leaf: 1 g gives gold leaf with an area of about 0.6 m². Assuming that the gold leaf is uniformly thick, its thickness would be approximately 0.000 08 mm. How thick is this in (a) metres; (b) micrometres; (c) nanometres? Given that the diameter of a gold atom is approximately 3×10^{-10} m, what is the thickness of the sheet in terms of the number of gold atoms?

Question 22 What is the difference (a) between a hydrogen atom and a proton, and (b) between a proton and a neutron?

Question 23 The major isotope of the element magnesium has an atomic number of 12 and a relative atomic mass of 24.0. How many protons and how many neutrons are there in its nucleus, and how many electrons surround the nucleus?

Question 24 The compound hydrogen sulfide contains two hydrogen atoms and one sulfur atom. How would you write its formula?

Question 25 Identify the repeat unit (unit cell) in the 2D array shown in Figure 7.41. (You can assume this is just a small section of a giant array continuing in both directions.)

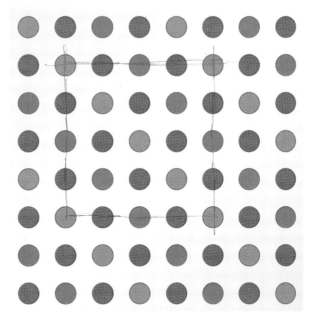

Figure 7.41
Geometric array for Question 25.

Question 26 Figure 7.42 shows ball-and-stick models of two isomers
with chemical formula C_6H_{14}. Which of the ball-and-stick models
shown in Figure 7.43: (i) are identical with one of the isomers shown in
Figure 7.42 (identify which isomer); (ii) is a different isomer; (iii) has a
different chemical formula?

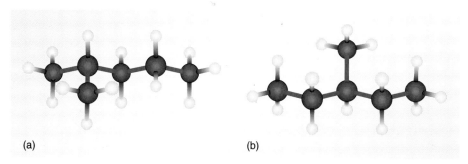

(a)   (b)

Figure 7.42
Molecules with chemical formula C_6H_{14}.

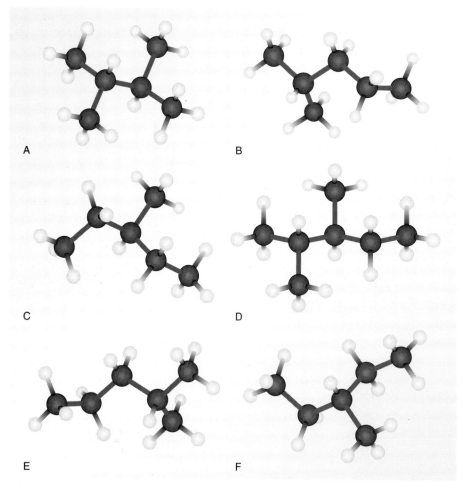

A   B

C   D

E   F

Figure 7.43
Ball-and-stick models for Question 26.

Chapter 8
Ensembles of atoms, molecules and ions

[handwritten margin notes: ie ton = one of its electrons / an atom with an electrical charge]

8.1 Introduction

All matter is constructed of atoms, molecules and/or ions in some combination or another. In a very short time we have covered, at least briefly, the structure of an atom, the attraction of protons and electrons, the covalent chemical bond in molecules, and ions and their packing in crystals. These are truly the foundations of all structures, from a hydrogen molecule, H_2, to the Taj Mahal and beyond. With the notable exception of crystals, in which many millions of ions or molecules are incorporated, we have examined only single entities and their structures. In crystals, the definite, repeatable and constant shape was said to be a result of the packing of ions or molecules in the crystal lattice in the most efficient way. Why should the ions pack in that particular way? That is an immensely complicated question: let's just say that, in general, chemical substances tend to find the lowest energy state that is available, rather like a ball on a bumpy surface will settle in a hollow rather than on a hill.

The organization of ions or molecules into crystals is a simple example of the cooperative nature of matter. The ions or molecules, without any external assistance, arrange themselves to form the regular and beautiful symmetry of a crystal. To illustrate that crystal formation happens of its own accord and not under external control we can look at the most usual way of forming a crystal. Substances, such as sodium chloride, that are soluble in water are not equally soluble at all temperatures and are usually more soluble at higher temperatures. In fact, sodium chloride dissolves to the extent of 36 g in 100 g of cold water (20 °C) and 39 g in 100 g of boiling water, so the difference in this case is relatively small. However, the related compound, potassium chloride, shows a greater difference. It dissolves to about the same extent in cold water as sodium chloride, 34 g in 100 g of water at 20 °C, but about 57 g of potassium chloride dissolve in 100 g of boiling water. (Potassium chloride, KCl, has a potassium cation, K^+, in place of the sodium cation, Na^+, in sodium chloride.)

▨   What do you think would happen if you took 57 g of potassium chloride and dissolved it in 100 g of boiling water, and then let the resulting solution cool slowly?

▣   As the temperature falls, the amount of potassium chloride that can be in solution becomes smaller, eventually reaching only 34 g in 100 g at 20 °C.

The consequence of this is that some of the potassium chloride comes out of solution as it cools. As it does so, it spontaneously forms crystals.

The way in which molecules (and some ions) organize, cooperate and assemble is one of the hottest research topics of our time. This research covers the traditional fields of chemistry, physics, biology, meteorology, astronomy and electronics, among others! We shall not be able to enter that arena at this stage, but many of the principles that are applied to such topics are also the ones that we apply to understand the nature of solids, liquids and gases. Only by understanding the kind of order or disorder that exists in these different states of matter can we understand the deeper problems of the nature of chemical and biological processes.

8.2 Forces between molecules

We have seen that the forces between ions are such that ionic compounds form crystalline solids. These forces arise from the attractions and repulsions between charged ions. But we have also said that it is possible to have crystals made from molecules. What are the forces between molecules that cause some of them to form crystals? We shall see a little later that the strengths of the different types of force between molecules determine whether a molecular substance is normally a solid or whether it is a liquid or a gas. Before we can do that, we need to consider what different types of force there are between molecules.

You may be familiar with the substance iodine. Commonly, a solution of iodine in alcohol, which is orangy-brown in appearance, is used to disinfect minor wounds. Pure iodine, however, is a dark purple shiny-looking solid (Figure 8.1). Iodine is an element with chemical properties somewhat similar to those of chlorine (Section 7.6), except that chlorine is a gas and iodine is a solid. However, just as chlorine exists as molecules containing two chlorine atoms joined together, Cl_2, iodine similarly goes around as molecules containing two iodine atoms, I_2. Iodine molecules are not ionic, because they do not carry a positive or negative charge. What, then, is the 'glue' that holds them together in a crystal of iodine? To understand the answer requires us to think about the structure of molecules in a little more detail.

Figure 8.2 shows two views of an iodine molecule.

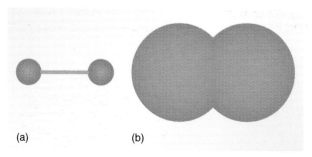

(a)   (b)

Figure 8.2
Two views of the iodine molecule, I_2: (a) ball-and-stick and (b) space-filling.

Figure 8.1
Solid iodine, showing its colour, shiny nature and crystalline form.

▓   What does the stick in the ball-and-stick view represent?

▓   It represents the covalent bond, which is made up of electrons that are shared between the two iodine atoms.

Now, although the ball-and-stick view enables the bond between the atoms to be seen more easily, the space-filling view gives a truer picture. The two intersecting spheres represent the cloud of electrons surrounding the two iodine nuclei. Remember that the electrons are negatively charged and the protons in the nucleus are positively charged. Remember also that electrons can behave both as particles and as waves. For now, it is perhaps easier to think of them as particles.

In an atom, the centre of positive charge is the nucleus; because the electron cloud is symmetrically disposed around the nucleus in the form of a sphere, the centre of the negative charge is also coincident with the nucleus. However, in molecules, it is possible for the centres of positive charge and negative charge to be separated. If this happens, the result is called an electric dipole, or just dipole for short: you can think of it as the electrical equivalent of a magnet. Just as one magnet attracts another because the north pole of one attracts the south pole of the other and vice versa (Figure 8.3a), the positive end of a dipole attracts the negative end of another and vice versa (Figure 8.3b).

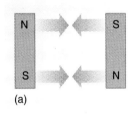 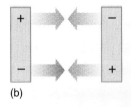

(a)   (b)

Figure 8.3
The attraction (a) between the north and south poles of two magnets and (b) between the positive and negative ends of two electric dipoles.

Let's try another thought experiment. In an iodine molecule, *on average*, the motion of the electrons around the nuclei is such that the centre of negative charge is coincident with the centre of positive charge due to the two nuclei, and so there is no dipole. But suppose we could take a series of snapshots of the molecule with a camera that had a shutter so fast that we could 'freeze' the positions of the electrons at any instant. At any given moment, the electrons may be more towards one end of the molecule than the other (Figure 8.4a). The next moment, the electrons will have moved and may be more towards the other end (Figure 8.4b). This rapidly changing situation corresponds to a fluctuating dipole. We call this a transient dipole. A simplified way of representing this is shown in Figure 8.4c.

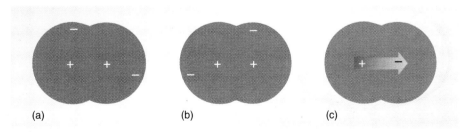

(a)   (b)   (c)

Figure 8.4
The momentary imbalance of charge as the electrons move around the two nuclei in a molecule of iodine at one instant (a) and the next (b). To simplify matters, only a single positive charge and a single electron are considered for each atom, but in fact each iodine atom has 53 protons in its nucleus with 53 electrons surrounding it. (c) A simplified representation of the iodine transient dipole.

Consider now two iodine molecules side by side in a crystal. If, at a given instant, the dipole in one molecule is pointing one way, then the dipole in the other molecule will point the other way (Figure 8.5a). This effect is called induction. As we have just seen, the positive end of one dipole attracts the negative end of the other, and *vice versa*. As the electrons move around the first molecule, the transient dipole will change direction. However, this will induce a corresponding change in the dipole in the second molecule, and again the two will attract one another (Figure 8.5b).

On average, the motion of the electrons around the nuclei is uniform, and so the two charges balance and there is no permanent dipole. But because of the relationship between the two transient dipoles, the *forces* don't cancel out as you might have expected. Adding up all these momentary attractions between each pair of molecules, the result turns out to be an overall net attraction. These attractive forces are called **London forces** after Fritz London (1900–1954), a Swiss theoretical physicist.

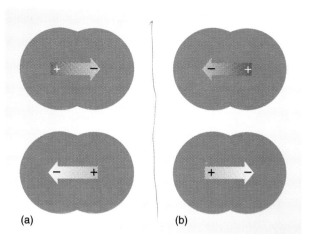

(a)   (b)

Figure 8.5
(a) The transient dipoles in two adjacent molecules point in opposite directions. This produces an attractive force. (b) When the transient dipole in the first molecule changes direction, the induced dipole in the second molecule also changes direction, and the two molecules still experience an attractive force.

The strength of the London forces between molecules depends on how easily the molecules form transient dipoles. Molecules containing atoms with many electrons form transient dipoles more easily (we say they are more easily *polarized*), and hence give rise to stronger London forces. The stronger the forces between molecules, the more difficulty they have in separating; in other words, the more likely they are to be in the form of a solid rather than a liquid, or a liquid rather than a gas.

▨   Does this explain why chlorine is a gas at normal temperatures and not a crystalline solid like iodine (chlorine atoms have 17 electrons as against 53 for iodine)?

■   Yes. The lower the number of electrons, the weaker the attraction due to London forces, and the more likely the substance is to be a gas rather than a liquid, or a liquid rather than a solid at a given temperature.

Other things being equal, larger molecules experience stronger London forces than smaller molecules simply because the larger molecules have more electrons. This point is illustrated in Table 8.1, with data for some linear hydrocarbons; Figure 8.6 shows ball-and-stick models of the same four molecules.

Table 8.1 Normal melting temperatures and physical form at normal temperatures for some hydrocarbons.

Name	Formula	Normal melting temperature	Physical form at 20 °C
ethane	C_2H_6	−183 °C	gas
octane	C_8H_{18}	−57 °C	liquid
tetradecane	$C_{14}H_{30}$	6 °C	liquid
eicosane	$C_{20}H_{42}$	37 °C	solid

electrons shared between two nuclei

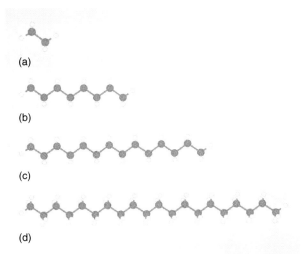

Figure 8.6
Ball-and-stick models of molecules of (a) ethane, (b) octane, (c) tetradecane, and (d) eicosane. (Remember the advice given earlier about not needing to commit names to memory.)

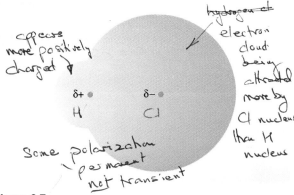

appears more positively charged

hydrogen ct electron cloud being attracted more by Cl nucleus than H nucleus

Some polarization permanent not transient

Figure 8.7
The unequal distribution of the electrons in the bond between two dissimilar atoms, such as a hydrogen atom and a chlorine atom in hydrogen chloride.

bond therefore called DIPOLAR or POLAR

molecules stick together more strongly

producing an attraction with other molecules called DIPOLE - DIPOLE force.

in addition to transient dipoles causing London forces.

So far, the model for covalent bonds has simply implied that the electrons between the nuclei are shared equally. However, they are shared equally only for bonds between two of the same type of atom, as in hydrogen, H_2, chlorine, Cl_2, or iodine, I_2. For bonds between two different types of atom, they are not shared equally. Some atoms in molecules attract the electron cloud towards themselves more strongly than others; they have more than a half share of the electrons forming the bond. Atoms that are particularly good at attracting electrons include chlorine, oxygen and nitrogen. There are others that you will meet later on.

Figure 8.7 is an artist's impression illustrating the electron distribution in a covalent chemical bond between two dissimilar atoms, such as hydrogen, H, and chlorine, Cl, in the molecule hydrogen chloride, H—Cl. The electron cloud is being attracted more by the chlorine nucleus than by the hydrogen, as indicated by the shading. The effect of this, to put it in a very crude way, is that the electron cloud surrounding the molecule will be uneven, and in some parts there will be a clearer view of a nucleus than in others. If there is only a 'thin covering' of electrons over a nucleus then that region will look more positively charged than a region with a 'thick coating' of electrons, which will look more negatively charged. These are *not* full charges as appear in ions, where whole numbers of electrons move from one atom to another. Hydrogen chloride is not ionic: it is a neutral molecule with no overall charge, and the number of protons in the nuclei is exactly balanced by the number of electrons surrounding them.

In Figure 8.7 the symbols δ+ and δ− appear (pronounced delta-plus and delta-minus), and these are the usual way of showing that there is some **polarization** of the electron cloud to give regions of *partial* positive and negative charge. This polarization is a permanent effect, and the uneven electron distribution is as much a characteristic of the molecule as its constitution and bond angles. It is different from the transient dipoles that lead to the London forces. Bonds in which there is a separation of charge towards one end are said to be **dipolar bonds**, sometimes just called **polar bonds**. Molecules, depending on the arrangement of their chemical bonds, can have an overall polarity, in which case they are called **polar molecules**.

There is an attraction between hydrogen chloride molecules because of this permanent dipole. These forces are called **dipole–dipole forces**. They are in addition to the attraction due to the transient dipoles that cause the London forces between all molecules. One consequence of the molecules of a particular substance being polar is that the molecules stick together more strongly than those that do not. The 'stickiness' is again a result of the attraction of opposite charges. You should be clear that both dipole–dipole forces and London forces ultimately arise from the electrical attraction between the negatively charged electrons and the positively charged protons, but in different ways. Dipole–dipole forces arise from the presence of *permanent* dipoles in a molecule; London forces arise from the occurrence of *transient* dipoles resulting from fluctuations in the electron clouds of molecules. Both types of force are essentially short-range and weaken very rapidly when the molecules move apart.

There is one further type of attractive force between molecules, and in many ways it is the most important. It is the reason why water is a liquid at normal temperatures and not a gas as it might otherwise be expected to be. It is also the key to the way in which the genetic code is translated. It is a very specific interaction and only occurs for certain types of molecule, those with hydrogen atoms attached to a strongly electron-attracting atom, such as oxygen or nitrogen. *Such hydrogen atoms form weak, directional bonds to similar strongly electron-attracting atoms in other molecules.* Although much weaker than full covalent bonds, because they are directional they are different enough in character to be given a special name: they are called **hydrogen bonds**.

In the case of the water molecule, H_2O, for example, the hydrogen atoms are covalently bonded to the oxygen atom and are therefore able to form hydrogen bonds with oxygen atoms in other water molecules (Figure 8.8). Because the hydrogen bond is directional, like a covalent bond, we denote it using a line; but because they are much weaker than full covalent bonds, hydrogen bonds are represented using a *dashed* line. Of our restricted range of building blocks, only nitrogen, oxygen and fluorine atoms attract electrons sufficiently to be able to form hydrogen bonds. In practice, nitrogen and oxygen are the elements involved in the great majority of examples of hydrogen bond formation.

Hydrogen bonds come about because oxygen and nitrogen attract the electrons in the O—H and N—H bonds so strongly that the hydrogen is almost totally denuded of electrons. Remember, hydrogen only has one electron to start off with. So the hydrogen is almost fully positively charged and is attracted strongly by oxygen and/or nitrogen atoms in another molecule. The four types of hydrogen bond that are of most importance are shown in Figure 8.9. Despite the very restricted number of elements that can form hydrogen bonds, because oxygen and nitrogen atoms are present in many molecules, hydrogen bonding is of great importance in the types of interaction that occur between molecules of a very wide range of compounds. You will come across examples of hydrogen bonding frequently throughout the Course.

We are now going to consider the make-up of different substances at the molecular level. In so doing, we shall use the models of matter that we developed in Chapter 7 and the concepts relating to intermolecular forces that we have just described. We shall examine what governs whether a substance exists at normal temperature and pressure as a solid, a liquid or a gas, and what happens when a solid melts to form a liquid and when a liquid vaporizes to form a gas. In all this, the guiding principle will be that it is the strength of the forces between atoms, ions, and molecules that largely determine these properties.

Figure 8.8
A hydrogen bond (dashed line) formed between a hydrogen atom of one water molecule and the oxygen atom of another. Note that hydrogen bonds are directional, and the three atoms are all in a straight line.

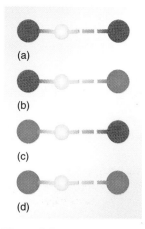

(a)

(b)

(c)

(d)

Figure 8.9
The four most important types of hydrogen bond:
(a) O—H– – –O;
(b) O—H– – –N;
(c) N—H– – –O;
(d) N—H– – –N.

8.3 Solids

The description given earlier of ionic crystalline solids, and by extension molecular crystals, implies that the components of a solid have a fixed geometric relationship to each other. Crystals made from ionic components are held together by the attraction of oppositely charged ions. Not all solids are ionic: for example, crystals of the element iodine are made of molecules.

In the previous Section, we said that the only forces between iodine molecules are London forces. These are sufficiently strong that iodine is crystalline at normal temperature and pressure. But, as we have seen, London forces between molecules are much weaker than those between ions. This is apparent when you compare the normal melting temperature of iodine (114 °C) with that of sodium chloride (801 °C)! As a general rule, molecular crystals melt at much lower temperatures than ionic crystals.

A more familiar example is solid water – ice. You have only to see snowflakes under a microscope to know that solid water must be crystalline (Figure 8.10). It must have an underlying order to give such beautiful shapes. The water molecule, as illustrated earlier, contains one oxygen and two hydrogen atoms with two O—H covalent bonds. The bond angle is about 104°, so the molecule is rather bent. These covalent bonds are very strong so the molecule retains its identity unless it undergoes chemical change in a chemical reaction.

Figure 8.10
Photographs of snowflakes under polarized light.

We mentioned in the previous Section that it is the hydrogen bonds between the molecules of water that account for the fact that it is a liquid at normal temperature and pressure. We shall look at that in a little more detail in Section 8.5 when we discuss liquids. Hydrogen bonds are also present in ice. The regular and directional nature of these bonds is illustrated in Figure 8.11, which shows part of an ice crystal structure. Two hydrogen bonds can

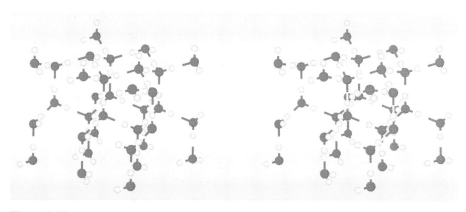

Figure 8.11
A stereoscopic model of the structure of ice. The water molecules are shown using a ball-and-stick representation to allow the relative orientations of adjacent molecules to be seen more easily. Notice that the structure is very open. In ice, the O—H bond length is 101 pm whereas the hydrogen bond length (O– – –H) is 175 pm, considerably longer. The hydrogen bonds are those coloured pink and white.

form to each oxygen atom. The oxygen atoms are then surrounded by four atoms in a kind of tetrahedral array, such as you have seen for methane. The arrangement is not exactly tetrahedral because two of the bonds to hydrogen are shorter covalent bonds and the other two are longer hydrogen bonds (Figure 8.11).

The sorts of solid that we have seen so far are all crystalline. One kind is the ionic crystals that are made up of collections of ions. The other sort is the crystals made from aggregates of molecules, which we call, with our customary precision and imagination, molecular crystals. An example of another type of crystal is the metal, gold (Figure 7.5). Metals have regular crystalline forms, and we shall study them in more detail in Book 2. A further type of crystal is one in which all of the atoms are joined together by covalent bonds. One such example is the mineral quartz (Figure 8.12). The quartz crystal is an essentially infinite array of silicon–oxygen–silicon (Si—O—Si) bonds based on tetrahedral silicon centres (Figure 8.13). Each crystal of this type is therefore a single giant molecule, though it is still made up of repeating unit cells.

Figure 8.12
Quartz crystals.

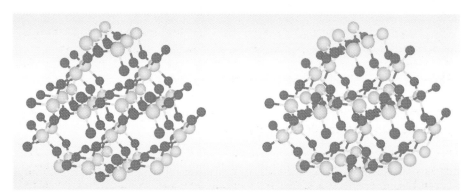

Figure 8.13
Stereoscopic model of a quartz crystal. The ball-and-stick representation is used to allow the crystal structure to be seen more easily. The silicon atoms are coloured silver and the oxygen atoms are red.

In a way, giant molecular crystals are the ultimate expression of order in solids. Every atom bears a permanently fixed relationship to every other, and great force has to be applied to change the shape of the crystal. That is in complete contrast to some other solids, which do not have a regular repeated order and are therefore not crystalline. A piece of polyethene is a solid by our definition. It has its own shape and does not flow at normal temperatures. Polyethene is made up of very long (on the molecular scale!) chains of carbon atoms with many thousands of atoms joined together. In a sample of polyethene these chains are intermingled like a bowl of spaghetti. Except at the ends, each carbon atom is attached to two other carbon atoms and to two hydrogen atoms, like an extended version of eicosane (Figure 8.6).

▨   Carbon–carbon and carbon–hydrogen bonds are not very polar. What forces do you think hold polyethene molecules together?

▨   The attraction must be due to London forces.

Because carbon has only six electrons and hydrogen only one, the London forces between one atom in one chain and an adjacent atom in another will be quite weak. However, as we saw in the previous Section, the effect of weak forces is considerably magnified when the molecular chains are long. The data in Table 8.1 illustrate this phenomenon: eicosane with its chain of 20 carbon atoms is a solid; the other examples with shorter chains are either liquid (tetradecane and octane) or gaseous (ethane) at 20 °C. You will learn more about materials such as polyethene in Book 2.

8.4 Melting moments

All solids are undergoing some kind of internal motion in which ions, atoms or molecules are vibrating. A simple thought experiment illustrates this concept. If we could sit on a sodium cation in a salt crystal, what would we see – and what would we see a fraction of a second later? If you could sit on a sodium ion and look into the crystal you would see six close-by chloride anions (Figure 7.34). A fraction of a second later you would see *the same six chloride anions*: they do not move away from their positions in the crystal. They are not, however, perfectly stationary. A crystal is not exactly like a building where you expect the bricks to be quite still.

In a crystal, or anywhere at the level of molecules, ions or atoms, nothing is still; there is constant motion of one kind or another. The ions, atoms or molecules are jiggling around their 'normal' position. If you could climb into the inside of a crystal you would see frantic motion all around you, but nothing would be going anywhere! The hotter the crystal gets the more violent is this frantic, getting nowhere motion. However, there does come a point when something drastic happens.

If you heat a solid, energy is transferred to that solid. The way in which the extra energy is expressed is in increased motion. As more and more energy is put into the solid so the internal turmoil increases. Eventually, the forces that were acting to restore the components to their original positions are no longer strong enough to hold the structure together. For a crystalline material at a given pressure, at a precise and reproducible temperature a change takes place. There are three likely possibilities:

- a change from a solid to a liquid
- a change from a solid to a gas
- a change from one crystal structure to another

The most common and easy to spot event is the melting of a solid to give a liquid. That is what ice does when you take it out of the freezer. When the temperature reaches $0\,°C$ some of the hydrogen bonds that held the crystal together break and the ice melts. At atmospheric pressure, ice always melts at $0\,°C$ which, you may recall, is called the normal melting temperature of ice. (The melting temperature of any pure crystalline solid is constant at a given pressure.)

As you may recall from Section 6.3, water is very unusual in that it expands on freezing, and it is the influence of the hydrogen bonds that is the cause. Ice has a very highly ordered, and somewhat open, structure with two hydrogen bonds to each oxygen atom. However, that degree of order cannot be maintained in a liquid, as will be discussed in the next Section. On melting, some of the hydrogen bonds are disrupted. In fact, in liquid water, the hydrogen bonds are constantly breaking and reforming between different molecules. This allows the water molecules a greater degree of flexibility and allows them to come closer together than in the more open ice structure. The result is that water at $0\,°C$ is more dense than ice at $0\,°C$: $1\,cm^3$ of water has a mass of $1.0\,g$ as opposed to $0.92\,g$ for $1\,cm^3$ of ice. The mass per unit volume of a substance is called its **density**, so another way of expressing this is to say that water has a higher density, $1.0\,g\,cm^{-3}$, as opposed to $0.92\,g\,cm^{-3}$ for ice (see Section 5.4 if you have forgotten about units with negative powers). By contrast, in most substances the components are packed more tightly in the solid than in the liquid, so the solid is more dense (has a higher density) than the liquid. In that case melting is accompanied by expansion (Section 6.3).

Ionic solids will also melt to give liquids if sufficient energy is given to the crystal to overcome the net attraction between ions. As we have seen, sodium chloride has a melting temperature of $801\,°C$, which is very high. Ionic solids generally have very high melting temperatures because the net attraction between the ions is strong. A great deal of energy is therefore required to separate the ions and break down the highly ordered structure.

Not all solids melt to give liquids when they gain enough energy. Some, such as carbon dioxide, change directly into gas. Carbon dioxide is a gas at normal temperatures, and is the bubbles in fizzy drinks such as lemonade or champagne. You may also have seen solid carbon dioxide, which is known as dry ice. It is very cold to the touch as it is solid only at temperatures below $-78\,°C$. (Touching dry ice with unprotected hands is very dangerous as the moisture on your fingers quickly freezes and this can lead to frostbite.) At temperatures higher than that, such as room temperature, dry ice disappears in front of your eyes (albeit rather slowly), being transformed *directly* into gaseous carbon dioxide (that is why it is called *dry* ice). Liquid carbon dioxide does exist, but only at high pressures. The process by which a solid is transformed directly into a gas is called **sublimation**. (The opposite of sublimation, when a gas condenses directly to a solid, is called **deposition**.)

Apart from the change from a solid to a liquid (melting) or the direct change from a solid to a gas (sublimation), the third possibility we mentioned earlier was a change from one crystal structure to another. You would not readily see a change of one crystal form to another unless it was also accompanied by some visible or measurable physical change. A frequently quoted example of this phenomenon is the metal tin. Tin has one structure known as white tin that is stable above 13 °C; below that temperature it changes into another form called grey tin, which has quite different properties. This is reputed to have had profound consequences for Napoleon's attempt to capture Moscow. You will hear more of this particular story in Book 2!

Non-crystalline solids, such as the plastic polyethene, do melt but usually over a range of temperatures. The way in which the chains are intertwined and aligned will be slightly different from place to place in the solid. The attractive energy between the chains is not therefore uniform throughout the solid. There is not a single temperature at which the forces holding the solid together are overcome by thermal motion. So a typical plastic, such as polyethene, softens as the temperature rises, and melts over a wide temperature range. This contrasts with the behaviour of a crystalline solid. A crystal remains structurally intact until the catastrophe of melting, like the collapse of a house of cards. Have you ever seen, or felt, a soft ice cube?

8.5 Liquid refreshment

Figure 8.14
Hydraulic systems find applications as diverse as (a) lowering and raising an aircraft's undercarriage and (b) raising and lowering a modern lift.

Liquids are materials that flow, have a fixed volume (at a given temperature) and take the shape of their container. If you try to compress a liquid you will have very little success. Hydraulic devices, in which a force is transmitted from one point to another by means of a fluid, rely on the non-compressibility of liquids (Figure 8.14).

At the molecular level, liquids are quite different from solids. The regularity, order and fixed geometric relationships in solids are replaced by randomness, disorder and lots of movement in liquids. Figure 8.11 showed a fragment of an ice crystal. A photograph, or its molecular scale equivalent, of an ice crystal would show the relationship between the atoms. If you could stick labels on some atoms and then take two photographs separated by a second in time the two photographs would be the same, except for very slight changes of position from vibrations. The orientation of the H_2O molecules, and their positions in the crystal would not have changed at all. This is shown in Figure 8.15a, which is a computer simulation of the motion of the molecules in a crystal. By contrast, in a typical liquid the molecules (or ions) are able to move from place to place as shown in Figure 8.15b. They do so at speeds that are impossible to comprehend. For example, a water molecule moves approximately 2×10^{11} molecular diameters in one second!

Figure 8.15
(a) Computer simulation of the motion of molecules in a crystal; (b) motion of the molecules in the liquid just above the melting temperature of the solid.

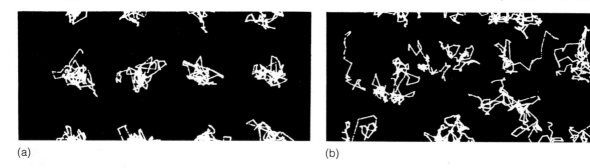

(a)   (b)

The components of a liquid are still in contact with each other, but they are constantly jostling each other and one molecule would have billions of contacts *each second* with other molecules. You can see in Figure 8.16 that the molecules in a liquid are not still: these pictures show the effect of placing some crystals of a purple substance called potassium permanganate at the bottom of a test-tube containing water. Over a period of a couple of days, the purple colour slowly diffuses through the water. Another illustration is the effect of adding a small drop of ink to a very still glass of water. At first the ink moves through the water leaving a trail, but after a while the trail gets very fuzzy and eventually the colour becomes uniformly spread throughout the liquid. So still water is not still at all!

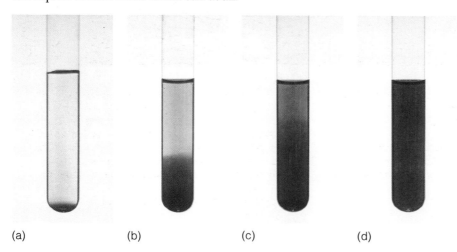

(a)   (b)   (c)   (d)

Figure 8.16
Crystals of potassium permanganate at the bottom of a test-tube containing water:
(a) shortly after setting up;
(b) after 7 hours;
(c) after 24 hours;
(d) after 3 days.

If molecules are moving as fast as we say they are, it may seem surprising that the ink drop is not instantly dispersed to all corners of the glass. But imagine a molecule in a sea of other molecules: if it moves in one direction then the chances are that it will collide with one of its neighbours and bounce back towards its original position. Just because the molecule is moving fast does not necessarily mean that it will rapidly travel long distances. If you are in a crowd milling around, even if you can move quickly you would have to change your path many times before reaching a specific objective on the other side of the crowd.

Box 8.1 Brownian motion

In 1827, the Scottish biologist Robert Brown (Figure 8.17) was looking through a microscope at (very small) pollen grains suspended in water. He observed a higgledy-piggledy motion of the grains as they seemed to dart back and forth through the water. At the time he thought that the motion originated in the pollen grains themselves, but that was not so.

In 1907, Albert Einstein (Figure 8.18) who made many brilliant and original contributions to science, explained the so-called 'Brownian' motion as the result of pollen grains being buffeted by water molecules, which are in constant motion. This was a significant contribution to the molecular theory of matter.

Figure 8.17
Robert Brown (1773–1858). Brown spent most of his life as librarian and keeper of the botanical collection of Sir Josph Banks, reputed to be the finest in England. On Banks' death in 1820, the house in Soho and the collection were bequeathed to Brown, who subsequently transferred the specimens to the British Museum as the basis for a national collection. He continued as keeper until his death.

Figure 8.18
Albert Einstein (1879–1955). This photo was taken in 1916. One of the greatest scientists of the 20th century, Einstein's career began inauspiciously when his application to undertake graduate study was turned down. Instead, he had to take a job as a customs clerk and to pursue his interests in theoretical physics as a hobby. Despite this, in 1905 he published three epoch-making papers, one of which described his theory of special relativity and included the most famous equation in all science, $E = mc^2$.

The molecules in liquid water are held together by the same kinds of attractive force as in an ice crystal though, as we explained earlier, there are fewer hydrogen bonds in a given sample of liquid water than there would be in the same quantity of ice. Nevertheless, the remaining hydrogen bonds still hold the molecules together strongly. This accounts for two special properties of water.

Most small molecules are gases at room temperature and pressure because the forces between them (London forces and possibly dipole–dipole forces) are insufficient to stop them flying away in all directions and assuming a gaseous form. Because hydrogen bonds make water molecules so 'sticky', water is a liquid at normal temperatures.

Another vital property of water is that it has a high **surface tension**. If you carefully fill a glass with water you can overfill it so that the surface of the water is above the level of the glass (Figure 8.19). If you have ever looked at a pond in summer you may have seen water striders walking on the surface without getting their feet wet (Figure 8.20)!

Figure 8.19
An over-full glass of water.

Figure 8.20
Water striders 'walking on water'!

These two examples are both manifestations of surface tension, which arises in the following way. In the bulk of the liquid any water molecule, which is rotating, spinning and moving to and fro, is going to experience an averaged 'pull' from other water molecules that will keep it more or less in the same place. Now think about molecules close to the surface. There is almost no attraction between water molecules and the molecules in air, because the latter are so diffuse. So the water molecules near the surface will experience a net attraction into the bulk of the water because those underneath and alongside the surface molecules are the only source of attraction (Figure 8.21). This attraction is sufficient to hold the water together in an overfilled glass and to prevent the water striders from sinking into the water. A further consequence of surface tension is that liquids with high surface tension, such as water, will readily form spherical droplets, either in the air or on an incompatible surface, such as a highly waxed car body.

When a molecular crystal, such as ice, melts to form a liquid, the individual molecules that made up the crystal still retain their identity though they are no longer arranged in an organized way. For ionic materials, the result of

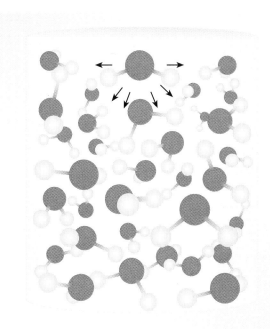

Figure 8.21
The forces on a molecule of water at the surface.

melting is slightly different. Although common salt is represented by the chemical formula NaCl, it is very important to remember that this is a shorthand and that there is no such thing as a sodium chloride molecule. As we have seen, sodium chloride is made up of sodium cations, Na^+, and chloride anions, Cl^-, held together by the attraction of opposite charges; they are not covalently bonded together. When the thermal motion in the crystal is such that the ordered structure breaks down (at the melting temperature), the ions stay as individual ions but are no longer uniquely associated with any other ions. The sodium and chloride ions in molten salt are free to move randomly through the liquid.

One of the main differences between the liquids that are produced from the melting of molecular solids and those from ionic solids is that *molten ionic solids conduct electricity*. This can be illustrated with the diagram of a simple apparatus for passing an electric current through molten sodium chloride (Figure 8.22). In this set-up, an electrical power source is connected to the two metal rods, labelled anode and cathode. The **cathode** is the electrode attached to the negative terminal of the power source, and so electrons flow towards it. The **anode** is the electrode connected to the positive terminal, and so electrons flow away from it. The effect of the movement of positively charged sodium cations and negatively charged chloride anions in the molten salt is to complete an electrical circuit.

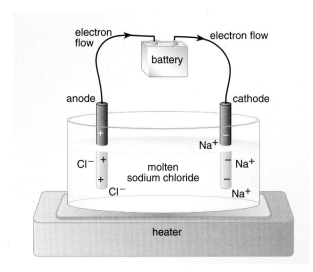

Figure 8.22
Diagram of a simple experimental arrangement showing the conduction of an electric current through molten sodium chloride.

■ In which direction do you think that the ions in the liquid will move? (Remember the forces that hold ionic crystals together!)

■ As opposite charges attract, it seems reasonable to suppose that the negative ions (anions) will migrate towards the anode and the positive ions (cations) will migrate towards the cathode.

That is exactly what does happen. In fact, that is how anions and cations got their names: anions are **ions** that are attracted to the **an**ode; cations are **ions** that are attracted towards the **cat**hode. But what will happen to the anions when they reach the anode and to the cations at the cathode?

If a circuit is to be completed, then electrons must be accepted by the (positively charged) cations at the cathode. In other words, the sodium ions must accept an electron at the cathode. When they do so then the sodium *ions* form sodium *atoms*. If you follow the logic of this through to the end, you will conclude that, to complete the circuit, electrons must be given up by the (negatively charged) anions at the anode so they can return to the power source. In other words, the chloride *ions* must give up an electron at the anode to form chlorine *atoms*. (These then combine in pairs to form chlorine molecules, Cl_2.)

The reaction that is described above is exactly what does happen, and this process, called **electrolysis**, is the method used to make sodium metal. It was the method by which Humphry Davy (Figure 8.23) discovered the elements sodium and potassium; a reconstructed version of the apparatus he used is shown in Figure 8.24. Metallic sodium, which is so reactive that it even reacts with water, is not found in nature and has to be made from compounds such as sodium chloride. The other product of the electrolysis of molten sodium chloride is chlorine gas.

It may not have escaped your notice that the production of sodium and chlorine in this way is the exact reverse of the reaction that we used to illustrate the formation of ions, the reaction of chlorine gas with metallic sodium. The main difference between the two reactions is that sodium chloride forms spontaneously, but to get the reaction to go in reverse requires a great deal of energy. The sodium chloride first has to be heated to over 800 °C to melt it, and then a very strong electrical current must be applied. Both these processes consume a lot of energy.

Electrolysis is a very common method for the production of metals, as you will see in Book 2. It relies on the fact that, when ionic solids melt, the ions have an independent existence.

Figure 8.23
Humphry Davy (1778–1829). Davy originally intended to become a doctor and became apprenticed to a surgeon. However, his growing interest in chemistry led to him becoming a research assistant to the chemist, Thomas Beddoes. Davy's publications brought him to the attention of Benjamin Thompson (Count Rumford) who offered him the post of Professor of Chemistry at his recently founded Royal Institution in London. It was here that Davy carried out his famous researches into electrochemistry that led to the isolation of many new metallic elements.

Figure 8.24
A reconstructed example of the apparatus used by Humphry Davy to discover the elements sodium and potassium, among others.

8.6 Solutions

A preliminary description of solutions was given in Section 6.4, but at that stage we were not in a position to discuss their molecular basis. Now, having examined the properties of liquids in terms of their constituent molecules, we can go on to consider how pure liquids differ from solutions. We shall confine our discussion to solutions in molecular liquids; we shall not consider solutions involving molten ionic substances.

In a pure molecular liquid, the molecules that make up that liquid will either be non-polar (that is, they are not polar) or they will be polar to some degree. They will be bound together in the liquid state by London forces and possibly by dipole–dipole forces and hydrogen bonds. The molecules are not completely independent of one another (as they would be in a gas) but they are not in a fixed relationship either (as they would be in a crystal).

When another substance dissolves in a liquid (and solids, gases and other liquids can all do so), then the structure and order within the liquid will be modified to some extent. The least amount of disruption will take place when two very similar liquids are mixed. For example, water and ethanol mix completely in all proportions. They both have O—H bonds in their molecular structure, and so can form hydrogen bonds with like molecules and with each other (Figure 8.25). The properties of a solution of alcohol in water are related to the amount of each that is present. For a solution involving two liquids, it is somewhat arbitrary as to which is regarded as being the solvent. We normally refer to the liquid that is in excess as the solvent.

Figure 8.25
Water and ethanol both have O—H bonds and so can form hydrogen bonds with like molecules (a) and (b) and with each other (c).

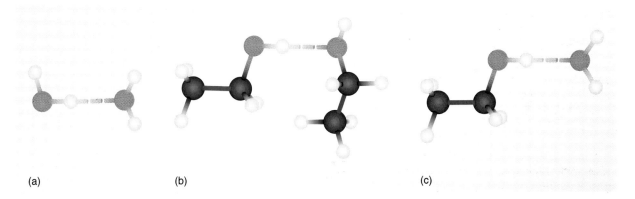

(a)   (b)   (c)

One property that is common to all solutions is that the temperature at which a solution freezes is always *lower* than that of the pure solvent. How much lower depends on the amount of material dissolved in the solvent. One of our Course Team had direct experience of this in Canada several years ago.

It was the heart of winter and I was invited to go 'ice-fishing' with a group of chemists. This, it was explained to me, involved going out onto a frozen lake, breaking a hole in the ice, lowering a line with a hook on the end into the water and spending the rest of the day consuming enough alcoholic drink to make you think you were warm and having a good time. "Bring along whatever you like to drink," said my friend. I took along a case of beer. "You won't be drinking much," said my laconic friend as we drove off. Within an hour of arriving on Lake Simcoe I understood what he meant.

*The others were fortifying themselves against the −20°C temperature
with liquors such as whisky and brandy containing 40% alcohol. My
5% alcohol content beer was not only frozen solid, but the expansion
on freezing had broken the bottles! I suppose I should have applied my
scientific knowledge in advance of the trip. But it is said that the best
way to learn is by experience. Now I know that whisky freezes at a
lower temperature than beer and that water expands on freezing. There
is not really a great deal more science to learn from that experience.*

The dissolving of alcohol in water is an example of a rule of thumb. The rule,
simply stated, is that 'like dissolves like'. Alcohol and water are similar in that
they are both polar molecules that can form hydrogen bonds using their
O—H bonds (see above). So, dissolving alcohol in water does not require
much in the way of disruption of the order and relationships that exist in
either pure liquid.

Let's look at two very different liquids, water and any vegetable oil, such as
corn oil or olive oil. The oils are complex chemical compounds, but they are
almost completely non-polar. A liquid vegetable oil is made up of large
molecules (with relative molecular masses some 25 times greater than that of
water) that are rather stringy and are held together in the liquid mostly by
London forces as the chains align themselves alongside other chains.

If you try to mix oil and water they separate into two layers because they are
almost completely insoluble in each other (Figure 8.26a). You see this in any
bottle of French salad dressing (Figure 6.18). Some hydrogen bonds between
water molecules would have to break to accommodate the oil molecules into
the liquid. In addition, the oil molecules would have to lose some of the
benefit gained by lying alongside similar molecules. In a solution of oil and
water (if such existed) both the oil molecules and the water molecules would
be in a more 'alien' environment than in the individual single liquids. The
best that you can do with oil and water is to make an emulsion in which very
tiny globules of oil are suspended in the water (Figure 8.26b). The oil forms
spherical globules because the sphere can contain the maximum possible
volume while presenting the smallest possible surface area to the hostile
outside world.

Figure 8.26
(a) A mixture of water and
corn oil showing the two
layers that form; (b) the
emulsion produced by
vigorous shaking of the
bottle containing the water/
oil mixture.

(a)   (b)

delta plus

delta minus

indicate some
polarization of the
electron cloud to give
regions of partial
positive and negative charge

Figure 8.27
The overall dipole of the water molecule resulting from the polarization of the O—H bonds.

The same 'like dissolves like' idea applies to solids dissolving in liquids. Generally, solids made from polar molecules dissolve in polar solvents. Cane sugar is polar, with numerous O—H bonds, and is very soluble in water (one volume of water will dissolve more than three volumes of sugar). Hydrogen bonding between the sugar molecules and the water molecules is very important. At the opposite extreme, our clothes tend to get soiled with stains that are greasy or oily in nature. These are non-polar so they are not at all soluble in water. The process known as dry-cleaning uses a non-polar solvent to dissolve the stains away. Later in the Course, you will learn how soaps and detergents help to overcome the reluctance of water to wash out such stains.

Ionic solids will not dissolve in non-polar solvents but are often soluble, to a greater or lesser extent, in water. For an ionic solid to dissolve in a solvent, the ions have to be separated and the orderly arrangement of the crystal is exchanged for the free-flowing form of a liquid. If the net attractive forces of the interactions between ions are to be lost in dissolving an ionic solid then they must be replaced by something else to compensate. In water, a very strong interaction called **solvation** occurs between the water molecules and the ions. You will recall from our discussion of the formation of hydrogen bonds that the oxygen atom attracts electrons strongly. As well as being the reason for hydrogen bond formation, this also means that the two O—H bonds in a water molecule are permanently polarized in the sense $^{\delta-}O—H^{\delta+}$. The two bond dipoles then add together to give an overall dipole for the water molecule (Figure 8.27). So when an ionic substance dissolves in water, the water molecules arrange themselves around the ions with the appropriate ends of the water dipole approaching the positive and negative ions. Figure 8.28 illustrates how this happens for sodium cations and chloride anions when sodium chloride is dissolved in water.

Hydrogen +

oxygen −

Figure 8.28
Solvation of a sodium cation and a chloride anion by water molecules.

Box 8.2 Purity

The idea of a pure substance has come up several times already. This has usually been in the context of a sample of a substance in which only one type of atom or molecule or ionic compound has been present. Although it certainly has not been stated explicitly, you might have gained the impression that 100% purity is possible. In practice, that is impossible. Any substance, however prepared, extracted or found, will contain some 'impurities'. This topic is covered in some detail when we come to look at foods, where the concept of purity is frequently confused with that of adulteration of naturally occurring mixtures, such as orange juice.

One of the purest substances available is probably the highly refined elemental silicon that goes into computer chips, such as the one driving the machine on which I am writing this Book. The silicon used for this purpose is 99.999 999% pure. Most things are considered to be very pure if they contain one single substance to the extent of 99.99%. Even at that level of purity one gram of water could contain about 10^{18} impurity molecules or ions! (That is not as bad as it sounds when you realize that one gram of water contains 3×10^{22} molecules, but it is still a large number of particles.)

8.7 Vaporization

The amount of motion in the components of a substance increases as the temperature increases, and there is a jump in the extent of the motion each time a substance changes from solid to liquid and then from liquid to gas.

▨ What happens to the volume when a fixed amount of a liquid is heated?

▉ The volume of a liquid increases on heating.

The expansion of a liquid as it is heated is a manifestation of the increased internal motion within the liquid. The energy transferred on heating manifests itself at the atomic or molecular level as an increase in the chaotic motion of atoms and molecules. The higher the temperature, the more vigorous the movement of the atoms or molecules. Each atom or molecule can be visualized as taking up a bit more space, and the volume occupied by the whole liquid will thus increase.

As a result of this increased motion, the forces between the molecules are more readily overcome in hotter liquids. When a certain temperature is reached, the attractive forces are no longer sufficient to hold the agitated and energetic molecules together in the liquid state. At this point, the extra energy no longer goes into increasing the temperature of the liquid: however much you heat it, the only effect is to increase the rate at which conversion into gas takes place. The temperature at which this occurs is the **boiling temperature** of the liquid.

If you were to go into your kitchen and measure the temperature at which water boiled, it would be about 100 °C. The freezing temperature of pure water in your kitchen would be very, very close to 0 °C. I cannot be more precise about the boiling temperature because it is much more susceptible to the external pressure (in this case the atmospheric pressure) than is the melting temperature.

The definition of a boiling liquid is one in which the pressure of the gas that is produced (called its **vapour pressure**) is the same as the pressure of the surroundings. If the external pressure is high, then the temperature of the liquid has to be higher for it to boil. Conversely, if the pressure is very low, then the temperature of the liquid can be relatively low for boiling to take place. An example that is more often cited than tried is the problem of boiling an egg at the summit of Mount Everest. As the atmospheric pressure is very low at the altitude of Mount Everest, the boiling temperature of water is much depressed below 100 °C and is in fact about 71 °C. Thus, an egg that takes 4 minutes to cook in Milton Keynes could take 30 minutes or more on Everest. However, the inability to cook a decent boiled egg on Everest does not appear to have diminished the number of climbers who ascend the mountain every year!

Of more practical use in the home is the increased boiling temperature of water at high pressures. Food cooks faster at higher temperatures. No matter how much you heat your vegetable water in an open pan the temperature will not rise above the normal boiling temperature of 100 °C or thereabouts. Some of you may own a device that allows you to cook your vegetables in a short time. I am referring to a pressure cooker, which is a pan that can be closed and a weight placed over the only exit. The weight is connected with a valve so that the pressure inside the cooker is fixed, as long as sufficient heat is supplied. If too much heat is supplied the valve allows excess steam to vent from the pan. The increase in pressure inside the pan means that the water boils at a higher temperature and the pan is also filled with steam at the higher temperature. As the temperature is higher, so the food cooks more quickly.

8.8 Gases

Liquids retain some order in their structure. A liquid flows and has a fixed volume. Both of these observations imply that there is some sort of interaction between the molecules (or ions) in the liquid state. Gases do not show either of these properties. A gas is something that pervades all the available space in an even manner. On average, matter is uniformly distributed throughout the space occupied by a gas.

To a good approximation, the individual atoms or molecules in a gas effectively behave as though they are independent of any of the other atoms or molecules in the surroundings; they fly through the void in straight lines until they meet another when they collide and bounce away, as if in a non-stop, three-dimensional snooker game. The number of collisions is still enormous by everyday standards, but compared with a liquid, the distances that molecules travel between collisions is much greater. The expansion in volume in the change from a liquid to a gas depends on the size of the container, as a gas will fill all the space available. But as we saw in Chapter 6, even at atmospheric pressure, one litre of water would give more than a thousand litres of steam.

Liquids and solids are not readily compressed. In contrast, because a gas will expand to fill any space that is available, it must also follow that a gas can be compressed. When the volume of a fixed amount of gas is changed the number of molecules remains the same, but the space they occupy changes. That means that the pressure of the gas will change. At a given temperature the pressure of a gas is related to the number of molecules in each unit of volume. Think of a bicycle pump. With each stroke of the pump, you decrease the volume of the air in the pump. Since there are still the same number of molecules of gas in the pump, the pressure increases. For example,

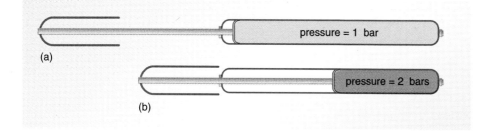

Figure 8.29
A bicycle pump: (a) at the start of the stroke; (b) when the initial volume of air has been halved. Halving the volume of air will double the pressure.

halving the volume doubles the pressure (Figure 8.29). As you continue to pump, the pressure eventually exceeds that of the air in the tyre, the valve opens, and more air is pumped in. Gases can be forced into a smaller volume by compression, but if the pressure increases beyond a certain point then there will be a change of state, usually to a liquid. The conversion of a gas into a liquid is called **condensation.**

There are some relationships, hypotheses or laws in science that can reconcile many apparently disparate observations and assume a central role in both the history and the practice of science. One of these is **Avogadro's hypothesis** (named after Amadeo Avogadro (1776–1856)), which asserts that *equal volumes of gas, at the same temperature and pressure, contain equal numbers of molecules.* The simplicity and elegance of this hypothesis is breathtaking, particularly when you realize that it was put forward in 1811 when the very existence of atoms and molecules was still hotly disputed by the chemical establishment.

The consequences of this hypothesis (which with modern techniques has been shown to be valid under most circumstances) are profound. Its role in the history of chemistry was crucial in helping chemists to understand the way in which atoms and molecules combine. It showed that the formula of water must be H_2O, not HO as Dalton had thought.

Activity 12 Verifying Avogadro's hypothesis – an exercise with graphs

By using some simple apparatus, together with a chemical balance that can weigh very accurately, it is possible to demonstrate the validity of Avogadro's hypothesis. Avogadro would not have had the benefit of modern balances, and so formulating the hypothesis in the first place was a considerable achievement. The test involves weighing a flask containing a number of different gases. The flask has special stoppers with stopcocks that allow gases to be let into the flask or pumped out (Figure 8.30a).

The flask can be evacuated by attaching a vacuum pump, and the stopcocks closed. By weighing the evacuated sealed flask, the mass of the flask with no gas inside can be determined. One at a time, a number of different gases are then let into the flask in such a way that the gas is at atmospheric pressure each time. The flask is then weighed. By subtracting the mass of the evacuated flask from the mass of the flask with one of the gases inside, the mass of the gas can be found. Finally, in order to determine the volume of the flask filled by the gas, the flask is filled with water to the stopcock taps. The volume of water is then measured using a measuring cylinder

(Figure 8.30b). Measurement of the volume of the flask using this method showed it to be 157 cm^3. The temperature at which the measurements were taken was 25 °C.

Some typical results are given in Table 8.2, along with the relative molecular mass of each gas. If Avogadro's hypothesis is valid, then the same number of molecules of gas will be in each sample because

(a)

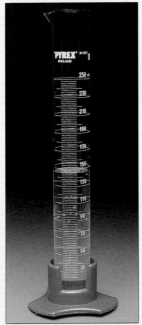

(b)

Figure 8.30
(a) Flask for testing Avogadro's hypothesis; (b) measuring cylinder used to determine the volume of the flask.

we are measuring the masses of a constant volume at a constant pressure. The masses should then be in proportion to their relative molecular masses. For example, oxygen, O_2, has a relative molecular mass of 32.0, and methane, CH_4, has a relative molecular mass of 16.0. If Avogadro's hypothesis is valid, then the mass of the methane sample should be half the mass of the oxygen sample because there are the same number of molecules of methane as there molecules of oxygen but each one has a mass half that of the oxygen molecules.

The masses of the flask containing each gas and the mass 'empty' are given in Table 8.2. You should complete column 4, by subtracting one value from the other as shown for hydrogen. Then check your results with the completed table given in the Comments on Activities Section at the end of the Book. Note that the building blocks of the element argon are individual atoms, not

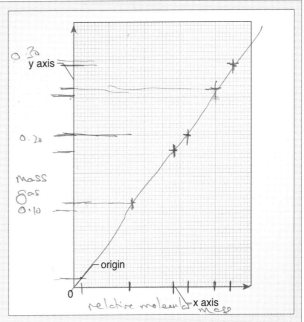

Figure 8.31
Axes for a graph.

molecules like oxygen or nitrogen. You will find out in Chapter 9 why this happens.

A good way to see if the data in the table support Avogadro's hypothesis is to draw a **graph** (a pictorial representation of the data). But what sort of graph do we need? When we have two sets of values for two properties and we want to see if they are related, then the normal

procedure is to plot one value against the other for each pair, or substance as it is in this case. If you have had little or no experience of drawing graphs, then this may seem a daunting task. In fact it is very straightforward.

First, using a piece of **graph paper** (paper inscribed with squares specially designed for plotting graphs), you need to draw two lines at right angles, one from a point near the bottom left-hand corner of the paper and going to the right, the other from the same point and going upwards. The two lines are called **axes**, and the point where they meet is called the **origin** (Figure 8.31).

Generally, the origin is where the values of both properties are zero. The

Table 8.2 Results from weighing gases

Substance	Mass of flask containing fixed volume of gas	Mass of evacuated flask	Mass of gas	Relative molecular mass of substance	
hydrogen, H_2	144.174 g	144.162 g	0.012 g	2.0	6
methane, CH_4	144.275 g	144.162 g	0.113	16.0	7.1
nitrogen, N_2	144.342 g	144.162 g	0.180	28.0	6.4
oxygen, O_2	144.363 g	144.162 g	0.201	32.0	6.3
argon, Ar — atoms	144.422 g	144.162 g	0.260	39.9	6.5
carbon dioxide, CO_2	144.452 g	144.162 g	0.290	44.0	6.6

horizontal line is commonly called the **x axis**, and the vertical line is called the **y axis**.

For the data in Table 8.2, we first have to decide which property will be plotted using the x axis and which using the y axis. Generally, the property plotted along the y axis should depend on the property plotted along the x axis. Suppose that we wished to plot a graph relating children's height to their age: their height depends on their age, rather than their age depending on their height. So we would plot height along the y axis and age along the x axis.

▧ In this activity, we are plotting a graph relating the mass of the gas sample to the relative molecular mass of the substance. Which property would you plot along the y axis?

◼ The mass of the sample: this is because we wish to see if the mass of equal volumes of gas depends on the relative molecular mass, not the other way around.

The other thing we need to decide is what range of values there is in the data, so that the scales on the graph are as clear as possible: too small, and the graph will be crowded down near the origin; too large, and the graph won't fit on the paper. For the relative molecular masses we have values ranging from 2.0 to 44.0, and for the masses we have values from 0.012 g to 0.290 g.

▧ Which of the following scale ranges for the x values do you think would be most appropriate: (i) 0.0 to 20.0; (ii) 0.0 to 44.0; (iii) 0.0 to 50.0; (iv) 0.0 to 100.0?

◼ The most appropriate would be (iii). With (i), it would not be possible to plot the data for the gases with relative molecular masses greater than 20.0; range (ii) would be possible, but normally the scale range is chosen to the next highest major division, in this case to the next highest ten, namely 50.0; range (iv) would also be possible, but would waste space as there are no values greater than 44.0.

▧ What would be the most appropriate scale range for the y values?

◼ Following the same type of logic, the most suitable range would be 0.000 to 0.300 (or possibly 0.350 depending on personal preference).

So we start by labelling the axes as shown in Figure 8.32a.

Each point on a graph is plotted using **coordinates**, just like a map reference. The x value is always given first, and the y value second. So the origin would have co-ordinates (0.0, 0.000) (Figure 8.32a); note that the number of noughts matches the data in the final two columns in the table.

▧ What coordinates would you use to represent the point labelled A in Figure 8.32a?

◼ (30.0, 0.200). The distance measured along the x axis is 30.0 units, and the distance along the y axis is 0.200 units.

We have plotted the data for you in Figure 8.32b; you should satisfy yourself that you understand why the points are placed as they are. For example, the point at the extreme top right has a value of 44.0 along the x axis and 0.290 up the y axis. The point is therefore just to the left of the vertical line through 45.0 and just below the horizontal line through 0.300.

From the graph, it is apparent that the points lie close to a straight line that goes through the origin. So the experiment seems to support Avogadro's hypothesis. The deviations from an exact straight line could be due to two possible factors: (i) Avogadro's hypothesis is only approximately true, or

(ii) they are due to experimental uncertainties. Given the rough and ready method of carrying out the experiment, the latter seems more likely. For example, we obtained the masses of the gases, relatively small numbers, by subtracting two much larger numbers; this is always a likely source of error. You will learn more about the whole question of uncertainties in experimental measurements later in the Course.

▧ By reading off from the straight line drawn through the points, what is the mass of 157 cm^3 of a gas with a relative molecular mass of 20.0?

◼ The line goes through the point where the vertical line through 20.0 on the x axis meets the horizontal line through 0.130 g on the y axis. So the answer is 0.130 g.

As you probably appreciate by now, in chemistry, we are particularly interested in how things happen at the molecular level. So, in many ways, knowing the number of molecules taking part in a chemical reaction, for example, is often of more interest than knowing the mass of material. That is why Avogadro's hypothesis is so important, because it

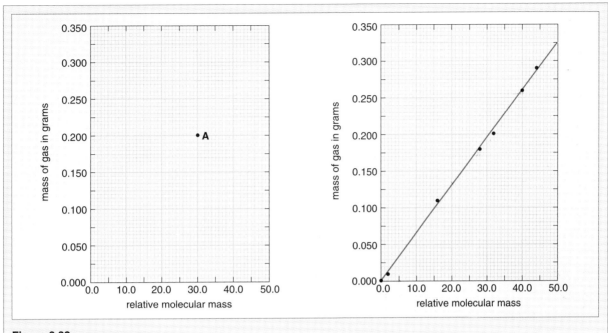

Figure 8.32
(a) Axes marked up ready for plotting the results in Table 8.2, with a sample point plotted; (b) a completed graph of the results in the table.

provides a way to do this without using the very large numbers that counting individual molecules would require.

■ According to the graph, 157 cm^3 of a gas with a relative molecular mass of 20.0 would have a mass of 0.130 g. What volume of gas would have a mass of 20.0 g? (Remember that 1 litre equals 1 000 cm^3.)

■ Since 0.130 g of the gas has a volume of 157 cm^3, then 1.000 g will have a volume of 1 210 cm^3 (157 cm^3 × 1.000 g/ 0.130 g). So 20.0 g will have a volume of 20.0 × 1 210 cm^3

which equals approximately 24 200 cm^3 or 24.2 litres.

In fact, more accurate measurements would have given an answer of 24.5 litres, so our measurements were not so bad after all! The answer to this question has provided us with the volume of a gas with a relative molecular mass of 20.0 that has a mass of 20.0 g. In other words, *it is the volume of gas that has the same mass as the relative molecular mass expressed in grams.* But because of Avogadro's hypothesis, 2.0 g of hydrogen, H$_2$, or 28.0 g of nitrogen, N$_2$, or 32.0 g of oxygen, O$_2$, would all have a volume of 24.5 litres and all contain

the same number of molecules. This number of molecules is given a special name: in honour of Avogadro it is called the **Avogadro constant**. The value of the Avogadro constant is 6.02 × 10^{23}, a very large number indeed! Because it is such a large number the amount of substance containing that many molecules (for example 24.5 litres of a gas at 25 °C) is given its own name: it is called **one mole** (the symbol for which is mol). Because there are 6.02 × 10^{23} molecules per mole, the units of Avogadro's constant are mol^{-1}.

■ Work out approximately what fraction of a mole of molecules is

contained in 5 litres of gas at 25 °C (about the size of an average toy balloon when inflated). Take the volume of one mole to be 25 litres.

■ Since 25 litres contain roughly one mole, 5 litres contain (5/25) × 1 mol, which works out to be 0.2 mol.

The concept of the mole takes a little getting used to, but once you realize that it is simply a way of counting molecules without the inconvenience of using very large numbers, you will appreciate its usefulness. You will have more practice with using the mole in Book 2.

157 cm^3 is 0.13g.
∴ 20 gm = $\frac{157}{0.13}$ × 20 = 24,154 cm^3
                    = 24.15 litres.

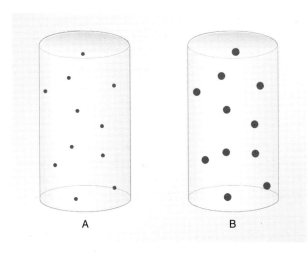

Figure 8.33
Diagrammatic illustration of
equal volumes of two
gases, at the same
temperature and pressure.

Let us look very briefly at what Avogadro's hypothesis means for atoms or
molecules in gases. Look at the diagrams in Figure 8.33, which illustrate
samples of equal volumes of two gases with the temperature and pressure
inside each vessel identical. By Avogadro's hypothesis, both contain equal
numbers of molecules (or atoms), represented by the eleven blobs.

Vessel A is filled with molecules that have a very low relative molecular mass
and vessel B is filled with molecules that have a much higher relative
molecular mass. The pressure in the vessels is measured by the force that the
molecules exert on the walls. This force is exerted by collisions of the
molecules with the walls. The force that a particle exerts on colliding with
something depends on two things: its mass, and the speed at which it is
travelling. The larger the mass for a given speed, the greater the force; and
the higher the speed for a given mass, the greater the force.

▨ Without thinking about specific speeds or masses, what do you think
Avogadro's hypothesis implies about the speeds at which the molecules
in the two samples are travelling?

■ If equal numbers of particles are applying the same pressure and one
set has greater mass than the other, then the speeds at which they are
travelling have to be different. It follows directly that, on average, the
more massive particles must be travelling more slowly.

If you have not understood the argument above think about how you could
apply pressure to a wall by throwing balls at it. You could either lob cricket
balls (160 g) gently at the wall or throw the same number of golf balls (45 g)
rather more vigorously. You would have to compensate for the smaller mass
of the golf balls by giving them a greater speed.

All this is rather long-winded way of saying that in a gas, on average,
molecules with a low mass move faster than ones with a greater mass, at the
same temperature and pressure. That conclusion is not immediately obvious,
but it has many consequences. Even in a mixture of gases where the total
pressure is made up of the combined contributions of the individual
components throughout the sample, the molecules with a lower mass are
moving faster than the ones with a greater mass.

To give a couple of examples: hydrogen, H_2, the lightest molecule, has an average speed of about 2 000 metres per second (2 000 m s^{-1}) in any sample of the gas at 25 °C and atmospheric pressure; at the same temperature and pressure, oxygen molecules, O_2, in the air travel at around 500 metres per second (500 m s^{-1}).

Summary of Chapter 8

Ionic compounds form crystals because of the net attraction between charged ions. Molecules, on the other hand, are not charged and so the forces that cause them to form crystals must have a different origin. There are three main types of force between molecules: London forces, dipole–dipole forces and hydrogen bond formation.

London forces arise from the attractions between transient dipoles due to the natural motion of electrons in molecules (a dipole being a separation of the centres of positive and negative charge). London forces are greater between molecules containing atoms with large numbers of electrons (high atomic number) or large molecules, particularly if chain-like.

Dipole–dipole forces arise from the interaction of permanent dipoles, which result when certain atoms have more than their 'fair share' of electrons.

Hydrogen bond formation occurs between hydrogen atoms attached to the strongly electron-attracting elements oxygen or nitrogen in one molecule and oxygen or nitrogen atoms in another molecule.

The guiding principle is that it is the strength of the forces between atoms, ions, and molecules that largely determines whether a substance is solid, liquid or gaseous at normal temperatures. Molecules containing atoms of high atomic number, such as iodine, I_2, have strong enough London forces to ensure that iodine is crystalline at normal room temperature. However, iodine melts at a much lower temperature than sodium chloride, which indicates that the London forces are much weaker than the net attraction between ions. As a general rule, molecular crystals melt at much lower temperatures than ionic crystals.

Examples of other types of solid are (i) ice, which has a network of hydrogen bonds between the water molecules, (ii) quartz, which has a covalent structure in which the crystal is essentially one giant molecule, and (iii) polyethene, which does not have the regular structure found in crystals.

When a solid is heated, the energy transferred goes to increasing the motion of the component atoms, ions or molecules. If heating is continued, eventually the forces that were acting to restore the components to their original positions are no longer adequate to hold the structure together. For a crystalline material at a given pressure, at a precise and reproducible temperature a change takes place: a change from a solid to a liquid, a change from a solid to a gas, or a change from one crystal structure to another. The most common and easy to spot event is the melting of a solid to give a liquid.

The melting of ice is unusual in that ice has a lower density than water at its normal melting temperature, whereas most solids expand on melting. This is due to the open network of hydrogen bonds in ice, which partially breaks down in water. This, coupled with the constant making and breaking of the remaining hydrogen bonds in liquid water, allows the water molecules to come closer together.

Ionic solids melt at a high temperature. Some solids, such as solid carbon dioxide, CO_2, change directly to a gas, a process called sublimation. Tin is an example of a substance that changes from one crystalline form (white tin) to another (grey tin). Non-crystalline solids, such as polyethene, melt not at a precise temperature but over a range.

Liquids are materials that flow, have a fixed volume (at a given temperature) and take the shape of their container. Hydraulic devices rely on the non-compressibility of liquids to transmit force. The structure of liquids is quite different from that of solids. The molecules move at extremely high speed and are free to wander throughout the total volume. However, collisions with other molecules mean that an individual molecule may take hours or days to travel a few centimetres. The strong forces between molecules in liquid water resulting from hydrogen bonding give rise to high surface tension.

In molten ionic solids, such as sodium chloride, the ions are free to move around independently of each other. There are no sodium chloride 'molecules' and no sodium cation is associated with any particular chloride anion. Molten ionic solids conduct electricity. If a power source is attached to two metal rods, which act as electrodes, electrolysis takes place. In electrolysis, the positively charged electrode is the anode and the negatively charged one the cathode: anions move towards the anodes and cations towards the cathode. When they reach the electrodes, electrons are transferred. In the case of sodium chloride, this gives rise to sodium metal and chlorine gas.

Solutions are made up of a solvent and a solute. Solvents may be non-polar or polar to some degree. One factor that determines whether or not one substance dissolves in another is the types of force that are involved. This is summarized in the phrase 'like dissolves like'. Solutions always freeze at a temperature lower than the freezing temperature of the pure solvent. When ionic solids dissolve in water, specific solvation takes place in which the appropriate ends of the dipole of adjacent water molecules are directed towards the differently charged ions.

Just as heating a solid eventually causes it to melt, the energy transferred in heating a (molecular) liquid causes increased motion of the molecules. This overcomes the attraction between the molecules and some of the molecules escape from the surface – a process known as vaporization. The temperature at which vaporization occurs throughout the liquid is called the boiling temperature. The boiling temperature of a liquid is greatly dependent on the external pressure.

Gases pervade all the space available to them. On average, matter is uniformly distributed throughout the space occupied by a gas. To a good approximation, the individual atoms or molecules in a gas effectively behave as though they are independent of any of the other atoms or molecules in the surroundings. Reducing the volume of a gas by compression increases its pressure. If the pressure increases beyond a certain point then there will be a change of state, usually to a liquid.

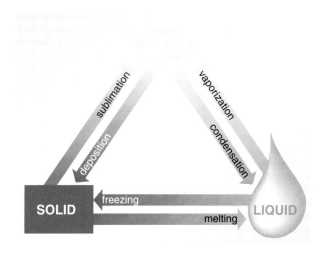

Figure 8.34
The various possible changes of state.

Avogadro's hypothesis that *equal volumes of gas, at the same temperature and pressure, contain equal numbers of molecules* can be verified by weighing a fixed volume of different gases at atmospheric pressure. Comparison of the masses of the gas samples with their relative molecular masses gives a straight line graph, from which can be obtained a value for the volume of the mass of gas equal to the relative molecular mass in grams (24.5 litres at 25 °C and atmospheric pressure), and hence Avogadro's constant (6.02×10^{23} mol^{-1}).

The various possible changes of state are summarized in Figure 8.34.

Question 27 The compound carbon tetrachloride, CCl_4, is a liquid at normal room temperature with a melting temperature of −23 °C. In contrast, the compound carbon tetrabromide, CBr_4, is a solid with melting temperature of 90 °C. By thinking about the forces between the molecules in each case, provide an explanation of the difference in melting temperatures. (Chlorine atoms have 17 electrons, and bromine atoms have 35 electrons. The C—Cl and C—Br bonds do have permanent dipoles, but because the molecules are symmetrical, the dipoles cancel each other out.)

Question 28 During the winter, the substance ethane-1,2-diol (also called ethylene glycol) is added to the coolant water in most cars to prevent ice forming in the cooling system. Ethane-1,2-diol, which has two O—H bonds in its molecule, dissolves in water in all proportions. Explain why a mixture of one part ethane-1,2-diol to three parts water acts as an antifreeze.

Question 29 A simple method of determining if a solid carbon compound is pure is to measure its melting temperature. If it is impure, the substance will melt at a lower temperature and over a range rather than sharply at a particular temperature. Why is this method much less useful for ionic compounds?

Question 30 Lithium bromide contains lithium cations, Li$^+$, and bromide anions, Br$^-$. If molten lithium bromide were electrolysed using the apparatus shown in Figure 8.22, what would you expect to see at the anode and what at the cathode? (Lithium is a shiny metal that is reactive, though less so than sodium; bromine is a red-brown fuming liquid.) Give reasons for your prediction.

Question 31 Explain the popping of popcorn (Question 19) in molecular terms.

Question 32 A flask at 25 °C is filled with helium at atmospheric pressure. The flask has a volume of 2.45 litres. How many moles of helium atoms, He, would there be in the flask? How many moles of hydrogen molecules, H_2, would there be in another flask of the same size at the same temperature and pressure?

CBr₄ – more electrons
∴ stronger forces between molecules ∴ more likely to be a solid
– greater London forces
– more polarizable

freezing temperature is always slower than that of solvent

ionic compounds melt at very high temperatures – more difficult to measure

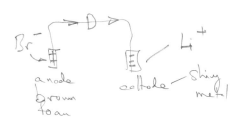

Br⁻
anode
brown foam

cathode – shiny metal
Li⁺

Vaporisation

– heat causes breaking hydrogen bonds

0.1 moles

0.1 moles

Chapter 9
Organizing elements

9.1 Introduction

Earlier in the Book, we mentioned that there is a finite number of elements that exist, 109 in all, of which 94 are naturally occurring. We also said that there are some elements that are similar in their properties to one another, whereas others are dramatically different. For example, we have mentioned that the element potassium is similar in properties to sodium, and that bromine is similar to chlorine. We have also seen that atoms of different elements can form different numbers of bonds: hydrogen can form only one bond, oxygen can form two, and carbon four. Finally, some elements form ions and others form covalent bonds.

It may well have occurred to you to wonder if there is some way of being able to predict all these properties: the reactivity of an element, the number of bonds it can form (what chemists call the **valency** of an element), and the type of bonding that the elements take part in, ionic or covalent. The answer, fortunately, is yes. One of the great challenges in the history of chemistry, the metaphorical Mount Everest if you like, was the classification and organization of the elements into a form that allows at least general predictions to be made about the properties of each.

Producing a workable classification of the elements was the towering achievement of the Russian chemist Dmitry Mendeléev (pronounced 'Mendel-ay-ev') who based his work, in the best scientific tradition, on empirical observations of the various properties of each element. As we shall see, beneath the pattern of behaviour that Mendeléev was able to discern is an underlying rationale. This depends for its understanding on the atomic structure of each element, that is the number of electrons and protons it has and how these are arranged within the atom. Before we look in detail at Mendeléev's work, let's remind ourselves of the names of some of the elements that we have already come across and their properties.

In classifying the elements, one of the more obvious divisions that can be made is between those elements that are gases, those that are liquids and those that are solids. This classification depends on the physical properties of the elements. In terms of their chemical properties, a more useful classification is to divide the elements into those that are metals and those that are not metals, referred to as non-metals.

▪ What substances can you recall that you think might be non-metallic elements?

▪ Some that have been mentioned frequently earlier in the Book are: hydrogen, nitrogen, oxygen, and chlorine. Others you may have thought of are: bromine, sulfur, phosphorus and silicon. (Actually, as you will see in Book 4, silicon is a half-way element with some metal-like properties in addition to behaving in other ways like a non-metal.)

- Write down the names of as many metals as you can that you think might be elements.

- Some that you may have thought of are: iron, silver, gold, tin, lead, zinc, copper, aluminium, sodium, and potassium. Slightly more exotic ones are chromium, nickel, cobalt, cadmium, titanium and manganese.

In answering this question, you may have written down bronze, steel, brass or pewter. These metals are not elements, however, but mixtures of more than one element. Such metallic mixtures are often called **alloys**, and the proportions of the different elements that they contain can vary over a wide range. Bronze is an alloy of copper and tin. Steel is mainly iron, but also contains some carbon and other trace elements; stainless steel also contains sizeable proportions of nickel and chromium. Brass is an alloy of copper and zinc. Pewter used to be made of 80% tin and 20% lead (Figure 9.1), but modern pewter used for household items consists largely of tin, with small amounts of antimony and copper.

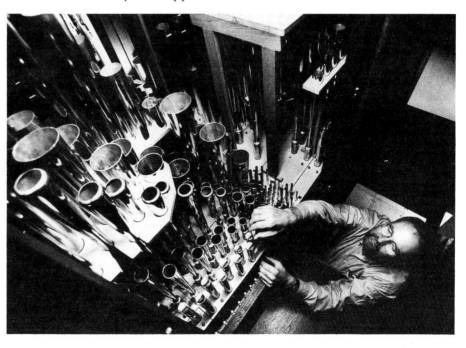

Figure 9.1
Making final adjustments to some of the pipes before the inauguration (1993) of the organ in the concert hall at St. John's, Smith Square, in London. Old-style pewter made of tin and lead is still used for making organ pipes such as many of the ones used in this organ. The alloys used range from 80% tin/20% lead to 20% tin/80% lead: the ones with high tin content give a bright 'organ' sound; as the proportion of lead increases the sound mellows and becomes more 'flute-like'.

It is the strength and relative non-reactivity of certain metals, usually referred to as **inertness,** on which many of their uses depend. For example, the use of metals in structural applications (bridges, reinforcement for concrete, hoists and cranes, aircraft, ships bodies, etc.) depends on their strength and unreactive nature. But we know from experience that some metals are not completely inert. In the presence of oxygen in the atmosphere, sometimes aided and abetted by water, many metals form compounds containing the metal combined with oxygen. Such compounds are called **oxides**. Steel (which is composed largely of iron), particularly it seems when in the form of car bodies(!), reacts with air and water to form just such an oxide, known commonly as rust. The rusting of iron to give iron oxide is a chemical reaction, and a very complicated one.

You might have come across another elemental metal, magnesium, which will slowly become dull on contact with air at normal temperatures as it becomes coated with a layer of magnesium oxide. If heated sufficiently strongly, magnesium will burn in air. It burns with a brilliant white flame, and so for many years was used in photographic flashbulbs (and probably still is if they are still made!). If magnesium is burnt in the open air, clouds of white smoke are produced. That smoke, which settles as a powder, is a compound of oxygen and magnesium called magnesium oxide, MgO.

You may have other observations about the reactivity of metals towards air and water, but mostly we expect them to be rather unreactive. However, there are metals that could never be used to build a bridge or construct a submarine. Sodium is such a metal. For one thing, it is soft enough that you can cut it with a knife. It is silver and shiny if kept away from oxygen, but on exposure to air it rapidly becomes dull and covered with a white bloom, which is sodium oxide, Na_2O. With water a more spectacular reaction is observed. A piece of sodium dropped into water skids around the surface fizzing and gets so hot that it melts into a ball (sodium melts at about 98 °C), and it can even catch fire! The chemical reaction produces hydrogen gas from the water, which the heat of the reaction causes to ignite. Sodium cations, Na^+, and hydroxide anions, OH^-, are formed in solution in the water.

One metal that resists attack by air and moisture even over a period of centuries is our favourite element – gold. Gold artefacts that have been buried in the ground or submerged in water for hundreds of years can usually be restored to their former glory by gently brushing off the grime and giving them a light polish (Figure 9.2).

Figure 9.2
The great gold belt-buckle found among other jewellery at the Sutton Hoo ship-burial site near Woodbridge in Suffolk. The buckle is made of solid gold, is 13.2 cm long and weighs approximately 415 g. The burial is thought to have taken place around 625 AD.

■   The metals that have just been discussed are gold, iron, magnesium and sodium. Look back at the descriptions of their reactivity with air and water and list them in order of decreasing reactivity.

■   The order is: sodium, magnesium, iron, gold. Sodium reacts rapidly with water and air; magnesium is slightly reactive but much less so than sodium; iron is oxidized only slowly; gold is inert.

This immediately raises the question, is there any way of telling how reactive a particular metallic element is likely to be? As you will see shortly, there is a way of organizing the elements that gives some guidance, at least, as to the properties of each element, by comparison with its neighbours.

If you were able to look close up at the atoms involved in each of the reactions mentioned above, you would find that they have one common feature. The reactions all involve the loss of one or more electrons from the metal atom. Much of chemistry is concerned with electrons being transferred from one atom or group of atoms to another. Metals, in general, share the tendency to lose electrons when they react, and pass them on to other groups or atoms. Some atoms, like sodium, lose one electron very readily, but no more. Elemental magnesium atoms will lose two electrons, no more, no less. Gold can lose electrons but that is more difficult to achieve. The number of electrons that a metal loses in certain chemical reactions is very characteristic and, as we shall now see, is the underlying rationale for many of the properties used by Mendeléev in his classification of the elements that is known as the **Periodic Table**.

9.2 Atomic structure and the Periodic Table

Much of what we know about the classification of elements is built on the work of Dmitry Mendeléev (Figure 9.3). Mendeléev was a wonderful chemist and an unusual person. He had a formidable appearance, mainly because he had his beard and hair cut only once a year. He is most famous for his periodic classification of the elements which, although it was not the first attempt to devise a method of bringing order to the elements, was undoubtedly the most successful.

Figure 9.3
Dmitry Mendeléev (1834–1907). A larger than life figure himself, Mendeléev's mother was also a remarkable character. After the birth of Dmitry, her fourteenth child, her husband went blind. She had to become the family breadwinner, taking over and running a glass factory. When the factory was destroyed by fire in 1848, she, at the age of 57, and Dmitry hitch-hiked the 14 000 miles from Siberia to Moscow and thence to St. Petersburg so that he could complete his education.

Mendeléev did not know about the electron structure of atoms; indeed, he didn't even know about electrons. He based his classification on the properties of the elements known at the time, such as the formulas of the various compounds that they formed. His outstanding achievement was to make a classification that also had great predictive powers. In addition to systematizing the patterns in the properties of known elements, it also allowed Mendeléev to predict the existence of certain elements yet undiscovered to fill vacancies in his Periodic Table. Not only was he able to predict their occurrence but he was largely correct in the prediction of their relative atomic mass and density, and the chemical formulas of their compounds with oxygen and chlorine. Mendeléev organized the elements into Groups and Periods, a model that has survived virtually unchanged to the present day (Figure 9.4). The Periods are the horizontal rows and the Groups are the vertical columns in the table. Elements in a Group have similar chemical properties; elements in a Period are in order of increasing atomic number.

One of the fundamental questions of chemistry is why different elements have different reactivities. Related to this are the questions 'why should some elements lose electrons readily and why should some gain electrons?', and 'what determines how many electrons are gained or lost?' We can't exactly say *why* these things happen; indeed, as you may recall from the earlier discussion of the scientific method, such a question is not within the realm of scientific inquiry. But we can, after centuries of observation, give a convincing rationale for the observations, and by understanding the physical basis, predict what is most likely to happen in new situations. As we have stated previously, much of chemistry is about electrons and their movements. It is the electron structure of the atom (that is how electrons are arranged around the nucleus) to which we look for guidance on reactivity.

The regularities embodied in the Periodic Table can be explained in terms of the way that electrons are arranged within atoms. Electrons don't just surround the nucleus in a great big blob of negative charge. The simplest model for electrons that helps us to understand chemical reactivity and the Periodic Table says that electrons occupy 'shells' that can each contain a fixed number of electrons and have different energies. The shells are numbered 1, 2, 3 and so on. Within each shell, the electrons are grouped into one or more sub-shells.

Groups (handwritten)

Periodic Table

1	2												3	4	5	6	7	8
1.01 **H** 1 hydrogen																		4.00 **He** 2 helium
6.94 **Li** 3 lithium	9.01 **Be** 4 beryllium												10.8 **B** 5 boron	12.0 **C** 6 carbon	14.0 **N** 7 nitrogen	16.0 **O** 8 oxygen	19.0 **F** 9 fluorine	20.2 **Ne** 10 neon
23.0 **Na** 11 sodium	24.3 **Mg** 12 magnesium												27.0 **Al** 13 aluminium	28.1 **Si** 14 silicon	31.0 **P** 15 phosphorus	32.1 **S** 16 sulfur	35.5 **Cl** 17 chlorine	39.9 **Ar** 18 argon
39.1 **K** 19 potassium	40.1 **Ca** 20 calcium	45.0 **Sc** 21 scandium	47.9 **Ti** 22 titanium	50.9 **V** 23 vanadium	52.0 **Cr** 24 chromium	54.9 **Mn** 25 manganese	55.8 **Fe** 26 iron	58.9 **Co** 27 cobalt	58.7 **Ni** 28 nickel	63.5 **Cu** 29 copper	65.4 **Zn** 30 zinc		69.7 **Ga** 31 gallium	72.6 **Ge** 32 germanium	74.9 **As** 33 arsenic	79.0 **Se** 34 selenium	79.9 **Br** 35 bromine	83.8 **Kr** 36 krypton
85.5 **Rb** 37 rubidium	87.6 **Sr** 38 strontium	88.9 **Y** 39 yttrium	91.2 **Zr** 40 zirconium	92.9 **Nb** 41 niobium	95.9 **Mo** 42 molybdenum	98.9 **Tc** 43 technetium	101 **Ru** 44 ruthenium	103 **Rh** 45 rhodium	106 **Pd** 46 palladium	108 **Ag** 47 silver	112 **Cd** 48 cadmium		115 **In** 49 indium	119 **Sn** 50 tin	122 **Sb** 51 antimony	128 **Te** 52 tellurium	127 **I** 53 iodine	131 **Xe** 54 xenon
133 **Cs** 55 caesium	137 **Ba** 56 barium	175 **Lu** 71 lutetium	178 **Hf** 72 hafnium	181 **Ta** 73 tantalum	184 **W** 74 tungsten	186 **Re** 75 rhenium	190 **Os** 76 osmium	192 **Ir** 77 iridium	195 **Pt** 78 platinum	197 **Au** 79 gold	201 **Hg** 80 mercury		204 **Tl** 81 thallium	207 **Pb** 82 lead	209 **Bi** 83 bismuth	209 **Po** 84 polonium	210 **At** 85 astatine	222 **Rn** 86 radon
223 **Fr** 87 francium	226 **Ra** 88 radium	262 **Lr** 103 lawrencium	**104**	**105**	**106**	**107**	**108**	**109**										

Lanthanides:

139 **La** 57 lanthanum	140 **Ce** 58 cerium	141 **Pr** 59 praseodymium	144 **Nd** 60 neodymium	145 **Pm** 61 promethium	150 **Sm** 62 samarium	152 **Eu** 63 europium	157 **Gd** 64 gadolinium	159 **Tb** 65 terbium	163 **Dy** 66 dysprosium	165 **Ho** 67 holmium	167 **Er** 68 erbium	169 **Tm** 69 thulium	173 **Yb** 70 ytterbium

Actinides:

227 **Ac** 89 actinium	232 **Th** 90 thorium	231 **Pa** 91 protactinium	238 **U** 92 uranium	237 **Np** 93 neptunium	244 **Pu** 94 plutonium	243 **Am** 95 americium	247 **Cm** 96 curium	247 **Bk** 97 berkelium	251 **Cf** 98 californium	254 **Es** 99 einsteinium	257 **Fm** 100 fermium	258 **Md** 101 mendelevium	259 **No** 102 nobelium

These sub-shells are labelled s, p, d and f. The first shell contains only an s sub-shell, which is labelled 1s. The second shell has s and p sub-shells, and these are labelled 2s and 2p. The third shell has s, p and d sub-shells (3s, 3p and 3d). And the fourth and higher shells have s, p, d and f sub-shells (for example 4s, 4p, 4d and 4f).

The four types of sub-shell can each hold different maximum numbers of electrons: s sub-shells can hold a maximum of two electrons; p sub-shells can hold a maximum of six electrons; d sub-shells can hold up to 10 electrons; and f sub-shells can hold up to 14 electrons.

- How many electrons in total can the first shell hold?

■ Since the first shell only has an s sub-shell, it can only hold two electrons.

- How many electrons in total can the second shell hold?

■ Since the second shell has both s and p sub-shells, it can hold two plus six, that is a total of eight electrons.

- How many electrons in total can the third shell hold?

■ Since the third shell has s, p and d sub-shells, it can hold two plus six plus ten, that is a total of 18 electrons.

The maximum number of electrons that each shell can hold is summarized in Figure 9.5.

Figure 9.5
The arrangement of sub-shells (labelled s, p, d, f) in the various electron shells (labelled 1, 2, 3, 4, etc.) and the maximum number of electrons that each can hold.

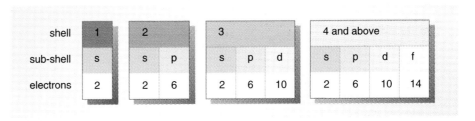

shell	1	2		3			4 and above			
sub-shell	s	s	p	s	p	d	s	p	d	f
electrons	2	2	6	2	6	10	2	6	10	14

The various sub-shells all have different energies. We can make use of this to see how the properties of the elements are related to the arrangements of electrons within atoms. Let's start by looking at a family of gaseous elements that are almost completely unreactive chemically. These elements are called the **noble gases** (someone has unkindly said that is because they share with the nobility a tendency to do almost nothing!). They form the Group that is placed on the extreme right-hand side of the Periodic Table (Figure 9.4), beginning with helium (He).

It is difficult to add electrons to the atoms of the noble gases to form negative ions; it is also difficult to take electrons from them to form positive ions. Equally, they do not readily share electrons to form covalent bonds. Indeed, they do not even form bonds with themselves. They exist as atoms, in contrast to the elements chlorine, Cl_2, oxygen, O_2, and nitrogen, N_2, which exist as molecules. They seem to have particularly favourable arrangements of electrons. These arrangements are referred to as particularly favourable **electron configurations**.

We can see a rationale for this stability by looking at the way that the electrons fill the various shells and sub-shells. The way we do this is by a 'building-up' process in which, for any given element, we carry out a thought experiment. We take the electrons in the atom and use them to <u>fill the electron shells one at a time</u>, beginning with the lowest energy one first.

■   What do we need to know in order to be able to do this?

■   We need to know the order of the energies of the various shells and <u>sub-shells</u>.

The order in which electron shells and sub-shells are filled is shown in Figure 9.6, which matches the Periodic Table in layout. So, taking each of the noble gases in turn, we can see how this procedure works.

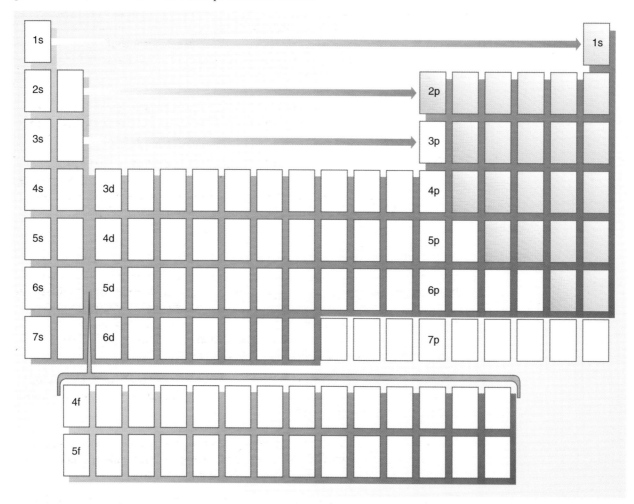

Figure 9.6

The order in which electron sub-shells are filled in the thought experiment 'building-up' process. *You do not need to be concerned why the sub-shells are filled in this particular order.* It is related to the fact that we are now in the world of quantum mechanics where ordinary, commonsense rules do not apply. Also, *you do not need to try to remember the information in this diagram and the associated text*. You will never be asked to recall this information unaided, and will be asked to use the diagram only to verify the arrangement of electrons in a given element.

The first member of this Group is helium (He), which you may have seen used to fill balloons. Helium has atomic number 2, which means that it has a nucleus that contains two protons. There are therefore two electrons surrounding the nucleus in a helium atom. The first electron shell has only an s sub-shell, and this is capable of containing a maximum of two electrons. We can therefore write the electron configuration of helium as $1s^2$, signifying that there are two electrons in the 1s sub-shell.

The next element in the noble gas Group is neon (Ne), which is the gas used to fill the tubes used to make 'neon' advertising signs. Neon has an atomic number of 10, and so must have 10 protons in its nucleus and must also have 10 electrons surrounding the nucleus. In neon, the first two shells are completely filled. As we have just seen, the first shell can contain just two electrons, and this is again written as $1s^2$. The second shell has both s and p sub-shells, and so can hold a total of 8 (2 + 6) electrons, making a total of 10 for neon. In shorthand, the electron configuration of the second shell is written as $2s^2 2p^6$. So we can write the full electron configuration of neon as $1s^2 2s^2 2p^6$, or slightly differently as $[He]2s^2 2p^6$, where [He] stands for the electron configuration of helium.

- The third noble gas is argon (Ar). Argon has an atomic number of 18. Using Figure 9.6, try to work out how the electrons are arranged in the argon atom.

- Since an atomic number of 18 means that argon has 18 protons in the nucleus, it will have 18 electrons. The first two electrons will go into the 1s sub-shell; two will go into the 2s sub-shell and six into the 2p sub-shell; then the remaining eight electrons will be divided similarly, with two in the 3s sub-shell and six in the 3p sub-shell.

So the electron configuration of argon is $1s^2 2s^2 2p^6 3s^2 3p^6$, or using the alternative way of writing electron configurations, $[Ne]3s^2 3p^6$. Now you can begin to see the virtues of the alternative notation; for atoms with high atomic numbers, it is a much shorter way of writing electron configurations. It is most useful for chemists because generally when elements react, it is the outer electrons that are involved in the formation of compounds. The outermost shell is often called the **valence shell**.

Adopting the same procedure for the noble gases krypton (Kr) and xenon (Xe), their electron configurations turn out to be $[Ar]3d^{10}4s^2 4p^6$ for krypton and $[Kr]4d^{10}5s^2 5p^6$ for xenon.

- It seems that the electron configurations of the noble gases must be particularly favoured, as evidenced by their general lack of reactivity. Can you see a pattern in their electron configurations?

- Each of the noble gases represents the completion of a Period, with the next element requiring the beginning of a new electron shell.

Now that we have looked at the unreactive noble gases, let's examine the electron structures of two reactive metals, lithium (Li) and sodium (Na). We have mentioned that sodium is particularly reactive with water, and lithium is also reactive towards water, although not so much as sodium. Lithium has an atomic number of 3 and so its nucleus contains three protons; there are therefore three electrons orbiting the nucleus of a lithium atom. In terms of the electron shells, lithium has the first shell completely full and the second shell contains only one electron, which is in the 2s sub-shell.

▨   What is the electron configuration of lithium written in full and using the abbreviated notation?

■   In full it is $1s^2 2s^1$; in the abbreviated form it is $[He]2s^1$.

Sodium has an atomic number of 11 and so has 11 protons and 11 electrons in the atom. The first and second shells are therefore completely full of electrons, and the third contains a single electron in the 3s sub-shell; its electron configuration is $1s^2 2s^2 2p^6 3s^1$ or $[Ne]3s^1$.

▨   Can you see the similarity in terms of electron structure between lithium and sodium?

■   They both have a single electron in the valence shell, in an s sub-shell.

The chemistry of sodium is dominated by the relative ease with which it can lose an electron. When it loses an electron to form the sodium cation Na^+, there are 10 electrons surrounding the nucleus *and the electron configuration becomes the same as in neon*. As we have seen, this electron arrangement is particularly favourable. Lithium also loses one electron readily to form the lithium cation, Li^+, and it achieves the electron configuration of the noble gas helium. So, to a first and very useful approximation, we can consider the attainment of an electron configuration corresponding to one of the noble gases to be one of the main driving forces for the formation of compounds.

> **Question 33** The third member of this same Group is the even more reactive metal, potassium, which has 19 protons in its nucleus. According to Figure 9.6, what would the electron configuration of potassium be? What effect will this have on its likely chemical reactions?

The elements lithium, sodium and potassium, and the others in the same Group, have one 'extra' electron over the number required for a noble gas configuration, so they can lose an electron with relative ease. In the dramatic reaction between sodium and chlorine to make table salt, sodium chloride, the sodium atom loses an electron to form the cation Na^+ and the chlorine atom gains an electron to become the chloride anion, Cl^-. Chlorine atoms have a nucleus that contains 17 protons, and this is surrounded by 17 electrons.

▨   How would you arrange 17 electrons in the first three electron shells?

■   Filling the first shell with two electrons leaves 15 electrons. The second shell will take eight electrons, so that leaves seven electrons. Of the seven electrons left, two will go into the 3s sub-shell and five into the 3p sub-shell.

So chlorine has an electron configuration of $1s^2 2s^2 2p^6 3s^2 3p^5$ or, in other words, it has one electron fewer in its third shell than argon, the nearest noble gas. The obvious way to attain the noble gas configuration is for the chlorine atom to pick up an extra electron – which is what it does in the reaction with sodium. So the chloride ion has the same electron configuration as argon, $1s^2 2s^2 2p^6 3s^2 3p^6$.

▨   The potassium ion, K^+, the argon atom, Ar, and the chloride ion, Cl^-, all have the same electron configuration. Why are the K^+ and Cl^- ions charged whereas the argon atom is not?

■   Although they all have the same number of electrons (18), the chloride ion has only 17 protons in the nucleus, potassium has 19 in its nucleus, whereas argon has 18.

We can deduce a great deal about the chemistry of the elements from the Periodic Table. The principles that have been sketched out in this Section are necessarily simplified, but they do form the basis for an understanding of the nature of chemical reactivity. In the modern Periodic Table there are large areas on the left- and right-hand sides where the simple rules that we have described work very well. In the centre of the Table a modified and more complex set of rules apply to electron transfer, and the electron structures are not simple. However, for carbon and a few other representative elements, a noble gas configuration can be achieved not by electron transfer, but by electron sharing. As we shall see in the next Chapter, this then provides an explanation for the formation of covalent bonds.

Box 9.1 Isotopes and relative atomic masses

You may have noticed that, for many elements, the relative atomic mass is not a whole number. Perhaps the most obvious is chlorine, which has a relative atomic mass of 35.5. If so, you may have wondered how this can happen in the light of our simple model of the atom, and the relative masses of protons and neutrons. The reason for this relates to the existence of isotopes (Section 7.3).

As the elements occur in nature, more often than not they consist of atoms of a number of isotopes in varying proportions. Sometimes, as in the case of hydrogen or helium, the element is almost completely a single isotope; in others, as in the case of chlorine, there is more than one isotope present in a significant proportion.

Earlier, we said that relative atomic masses are defined in terms of carbon-12 = 12. In fact, naturally occurring carbon contains about 99% carbon-12 and about 1% carbon-13, so the relative atomic mass of naturally occurring carbon is very close to 12. However, naturally occurring chlorine consists of approximately 75% chlorine-35 and 25% chlorine-37. So the measured relative atomic mass of naturally occurring chlorine will be an average value somewhere between 35 and 37. Because there is a higher proportion of chlorine-35 it will lie closer to 35 than 37. In fact, the value can be calculated by using the relative proportions as follows: $[(35 \times 75\%) + (37 \times 25\%)] \div 100\%$, which works out to be 35.5.

Summary of Chapter 9   112

There are 109 elements known, of which 94 are naturally occurring. Some elements exhibit similar reactions to other elements, for example potassium and sodium. Different elements form different numbers of bonds, and some elements form ions and others form covalent bonds. Bringing some order to the properties of the elements was one of the great challenges to the early chemists.

In classifying the elements, one of the more obvious divisions that can be made is between those elements that are gases, those that are liquids and those that are solids. But, for chemical purposes, a more useful classification is to divide the elements into metals and non-metals. Examples of elements that are non-metals are hydrogen, nitrogen, oxygen, chlorine, bromine, sulfur, phosphorus and silicon. Examples of metallic elements are iron, silver, gold, tin, lead, zinc, copper, aluminium, sodium, potassium, chromium, nickel, cobalt, cadmium, titanium and manganese. Metals such as bronze, steel, brass or pewter are not elements but mixtures called alloys.

Metals in everyday experience are strong and not noticeably reactive with air or water. These properties suit these metals for structural uses. None the less, they do react over a period of time with oxygen and/or water to form oxides. Other metallic elements, such as sodium and magnesium, are more reactive towards oxygen and water.

It is possible to place the metallic elements in an order of reactivity: one such sequence would be sodium (most reactive), magnesium, iron, gold (least reactive). A feature that metallic elements have in common is that they react by losing electrons to form positive ions (cations). The relative ease with which electrons are removed and the number lost are characteristic of each element. Properties such as these were used by Mendeléev in constructing the Periodic Table.

Mendeléev's great achievement was to make a classification based on the properties of the elements known at the time, which also had great predictive power. In addition to systematizing the patterns in the properties of known elements, it allowed him to predict not only the existence of certain elements yet undiscovered to fill vacancies in his Periodic Table but also many of their properties.

The regularities embodied in the Periodic Table can be explained in terms of the way that electrons are arranged within atoms. Electrons occupy 'shells' that can each contain a fixed number of electrons. Within each shell, the electrons are grouped into a series of sub-shells. The various sub-shells all have different energies.

The arrangement of electrons in each atom, called the electron configuration, can be obtained by a thought experiment involving a 'building-up' process in which, for any given element, we take the electrons in the atom and use them to fill the electron shells one at a time, beginning with the one of lowest energy.

This building-up process leads to the conclusion that the noble gases, the Group of elements on the extreme right of the Periodic Table, have a particularly favourable electron configuration. The reactivity of elements either side of the noble gases, such as sodium and chlorine, can be rationalized in terms of achieving the noble gas configuration.

A great deal can be deduced about the chemistry of the elements from the Periodic Table. In the modern Periodic Table there are large areas on the left- and right-hand sides where the simple rules described work very well. In the centre, a modified and more complex set of rules applies to electron transfer, and the electron structures are not simple. However, for carbon and a few other representative elements, a noble gas configuration can be achieved not by electron transfer, but by electron sharing in covalent bonds.

A summary table of the elements (giving their name, symbol, date of discovery or synthesis, atomic number, relative atomic mass, normal melting temperature and normal boiling temperature) is given in the Appendix.

Question 34 Using the abbreviated notation, write down the electron configuration of nitrogen (N). (You will need to consult the Periodic Table (Figure 9.4) or the Appendix to find out the atomic number, and use Figure 9.6 for the order of the electron sub-shells.)

Question 35 Using the abbreviated notation, write down the electron configuration of magnesium (Mg). (You will need to consult the Periodic Table (Figure 9.4) or the Appendix to find out the atomic number, and use Figure 9.6 for the order of the electron sub-shells.)

Question 36 Using the abbreviated notation, write down the electron configuration of bromine (Br). (You will need to consult the Periodic Table (Figure 9.4) or the Appendix to find out the atomic number, and use Figure 9.6 for the order of the electron sub-shells.)

Question 37 Which ion is likely to be formed in reactions involving the element aluminium (Al)?

Question 38 Elements in a Group of the Periodic Table have similar chemical properties. The elements in the Group that tend to form ions with a single negative charge are called the halogens. Which are the elements in this Group?

Chapter 10
The world of carbon

10.1 Carbon the element

Carbon is arguably the key element on which life depends in more ways than one. Human beings, and all other life, are based on carbon combined with hydrogen, nitrogen, oxygen and (a few) other elements. We depend for much of our electrical power and fuel needs on fossil fuels that are based on carbon. Many of our modern materials, such as nylon, polyethene, acrylics and other plastics, are carbon-based. So carbon really is *the* element at the centre of our chemical environment. There will be much about carbon chemistry during the rest of the Course, but in this Section we want to look at carbon in its *elemental* forms.

There is a rich structural chemistry exhibited by carbon in combination with itself. All the carbon forms that we shall look at are covalently bonded, and you will see an astonishing variety of properties and structures. The forms of carbon that will be discussed are diamond, graphite and a whole family of relatively newly discovered forms called fullerenes, or more often simply 'bucky balls'.

In stable compounds there are always four covalent bonds to each carbon atom. In Section 7.5 the four different carbon building blocks were introduced. All the diversity we have promised in this Section stems from just *two* of these building blocks, only one of which is used in each form. The two building blocks are (i) the one with four single, covalent bonds in a tetrahedral arrangement as found, for example, in methane and (ii) the one with two single bonds and one double bond as found, for example, in ethene. But why does carbon form a total of four bonds always, and not three or five?

▪ What is the electron configuration of carbon? How close is this to the electron configuration of a noble gas? (You will need to consult the Periodic Table.)

▪ Carbon has an atomic number of 6 and so has six protons in the nucleus. There are therefore six electrons. Two of these will occupy the first shell (the 1s sub-shell) and two more will occupy the 2s sub-shell. This leaves two to go into the 2p sub-shell. The electron configuration of carbon is thus $1s^2 2s^2 2p^2$, or $[He]2s^2 2p^2$. This leaves carbon four electrons short of the configuration of neon. Alternatively, it has four electrons more than the configuration of helium.

$1s^2\ 2s^2\ 2p^2$

$= [He]\ 2s^2 2p^2$

If carbon were to gain four electrons it could achieve the electron configuration of neon; alternatively, it could lose four electrons to achieve the electron configuration of helium. However, forming C^{4-} or C^{4+} ions (the 4− means four negative charges and 4+ means four positive charges) requires a great deal of energy, and carbon takes a different route. If, instead of acquiring or losing electrons completely it were to share them with another atom, then both atoms could achieve the electron configuration of a noble gas. This is exactly what happens with carbon.

Let's look again at methane, CH_4 (Section 7.5). It has four covalent bonds, one from the carbon atom to each hydrogen atom. The rule in forming covalent bonds is that only the outermost electrons (those in the valence shell) become involved: these are called the **valence electrons**. So for carbon, we need to consider only the four electrons in the second shell and hydrogen has only one electron anyway (Figure 10.1a). If we denote the electrons by dots, then the electron configuration of methane can be shown as in Figure 10.1b. The carbon atom now has a share in eight electrons in the outer shell, which corresponds to the electron configuration of neon; each hydrogen atom now has a share of two electrons, which corresponds to the electron configuration of helium. A crucial feature of this sharing process is that a covalent bond, which we denote using a line as in Figure 10.1c, consists of two shared electrons.

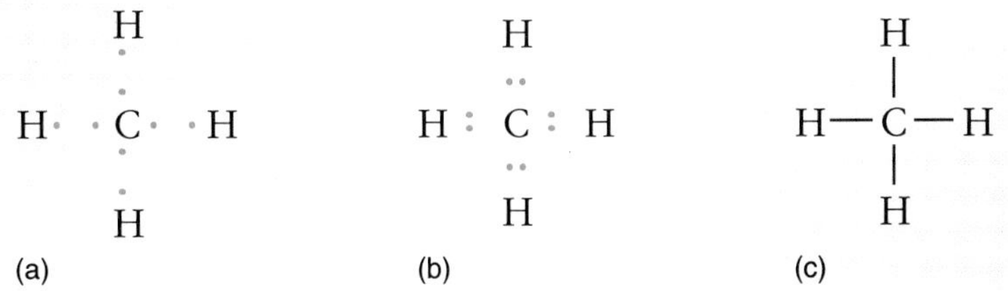

(a)   (b)   (c)

Figure 10.1
(a) The valence electrons of a carbon atom and four hydrogen atoms and (b) the electron configuration of methane, showing the sharing of electrons, with the electrons denoted by dots. (c) The four covalent bonds in methane, where a line represents a bond consisting of two electrons shared between the two atoms.

A similar situation occurs for ethane, which has the formula C_2H_6, except that this time there is a carbon–carbon bond as well as carbon–hydrogen bonds. The electron configuration of ethane is shown in Figure 10.2.

A slightly different situation is found in ethene. Ethene, as you may recall from Section 7.5, has the formula C_2H_4. In ethene, each carbon shares electrons with only two hydrogen atoms, not three as in ethane. Consequently, each carbon atom in ethene has to share two electrons, not just one, with the other carbon atom and so forms two covalent bonds, each with two electrons (Figure 10.3a). Since we use a single line to denote a single bond, we use two lines close together to denote a double bond (Figure 10.3b).

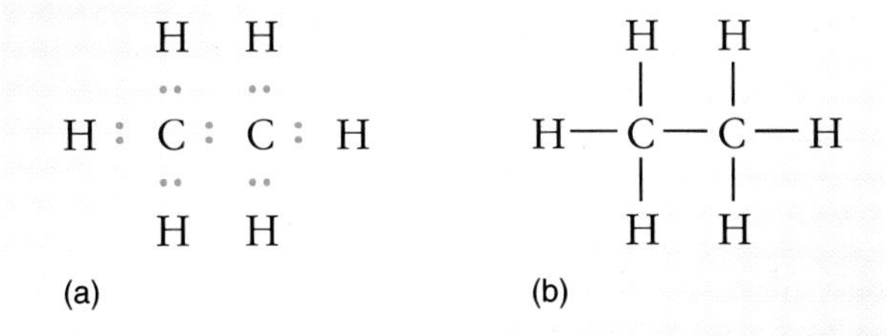

(a)   (b)

(a)   (b)

Figure 10.2
(a) The electron configuration of ethane, showing the sharing of electrons; (b) the seven covalent bonds in ethane, where a line represents a bond consisting of two electrons shared between the two atoms.

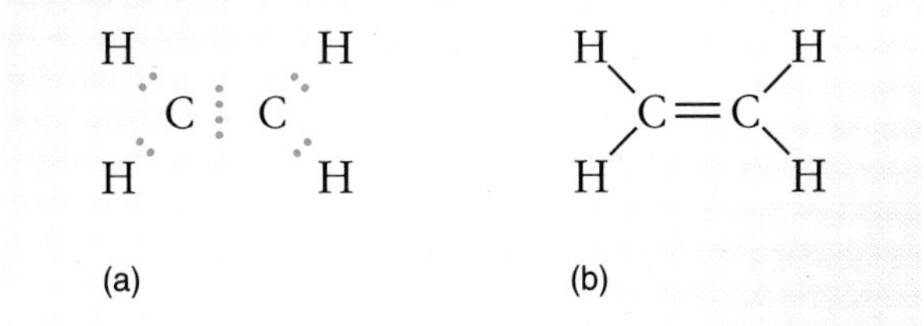

Figure 10.3
(a) The electron configuration of ethene, showing the sharing of electrons; (b) the four single bonds in ethene are denoted by single lines and the double bond by two lines close together.

This then is the process by which elements can form covalent bonds, and it also explains what determines how many bonds a given element is able to form. We shall now move on to see how the same units found in methane (or ethane) and ethene are the basic units of the different forms of elemental carbon.

10.2 Diamonds are forever

The only form of carbon in which all the atoms are joined together with single covalent bonds is diamond. Diamonds are found naturally in a rock called kimberlite. Kimberlite is a curious soft rock, which forms a kind of conduit between the layers beneath the Earth's crust, where diamonds are formed, and the Earth's surface (Figure 10.4). South Africa and Russia are two of the main sources of diamonds (Figures 10.5 and 10.6).

Figure 10.4
A rough diamond in kimberlite.

Figure 10.5
Diamonds occur in a number of different colours and grades.

Figure 10.6
A cut and an uncut diamond.

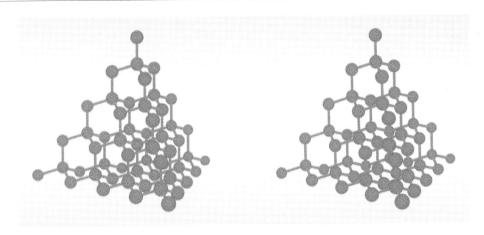

Figure 10.7
Stereoscopic model of the structure of diamond.

A part of the structure of diamond is shown in Figure 10.7. If you look carefully you will see that it bears a striking resemblance to the ice structure that you have seen previously (Figure 8.11). The other obvious similarity between ice and diamond is their brilliance – diamonds are called 'ice' in the underworld, at least they are in old Ealing films. Remember, however, that ice is made up of molecules of water linked by hydrogen bonds, whereas diamond is made of carbon atoms linked together by covalent bonds. In that sense, the structure of diamond is more like that of quartz (Figure 8.13).

This almost infinite array of carbon atoms means that each diamond is a single giant molecule. This is responsible for the very high melting temperature of diamond, which is greater than $4\,000\,°C$.

The cutting of diamonds is a highly skilled profession and needs a knowledge of the crystal structure of diamond. When a diamond is 'cut' it is not a matter of sawing the thing to shape. Diamond is one of the hardest substances known, so what could you use to cut it? As with most crystals, if you can choose the right direction diamond will cleave more easily. Earlier, we saw that one of the planes in the gold crystal has the gold atoms packed particularly close together (Figure 7.6c). This illustrates the idea that if you find one of those planes then the crystal will cleave more easily. There is a very limited number of angles available between the planes in cut diamonds, which accounts for the similarity in designs.

For those with diamond jewellery, the bad news about diamonds is that they have a natural tendency to change their form to the type of carbon to be discussed next, graphite, which is the 'lead' in your pencil! The good news is that the change will take millions of years at normal temperature, although it is measurably fast at temperatures greater than $2\,000\,°C$. In oxygen or air at about $800\,°C$, diamond will burn to produce carbon dioxide as the only product. Diamond would probably be a very clean solid fuel, but it is certainly not an economically feasible one!

10.3 Graphite

Graphite is found as a soft, grey-black mineral called plumbago (graphite resembles lead in a very superficial way, and the Latin name for lead is *plumbum*). At normal temperatures and pressures, graphite is the most stable form of carbon. The 'lead' in soft pencils is largely graphite (clay is added to make hard pencils), and that use demonstrates its soft crumbly nature. Graphite is also used as a lubricant for machinery. Although graphite is found in nature, most of the commercially used graphite is manufactured from other forms of carbon by heating for several days in a very hot furnace. The forms of carbon that are used in this process do not have a regular structure like the rest of the forms described in this study. They are broadly classed as **amorphous** carbon. The term amorphous is generally applied to substances that do not have regular crystalline forms; it does not necessarily indicate a complete lack of structure. Within the sample there can be areas with well-defined crystal structures and others in which there is much less structure. They are usually difficult to examine closely because of the lack of regularity. Just as diamond can be converted into graphite at high temperature, so amorphous carbon can be similarly converted into graphite.

The structure of graphite is quite different from that of diamond, although both are extended arrays of covalently bonded carbon atoms (Figure 10.8). Diamond has the ultimate three-dimensional structure, whereas graphite has the last word in two-dimensional arrays.

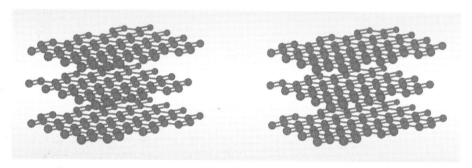

Figure 10.8
Stereoscopic model of the structure of graphite.

In graphite, each carbon has two single bonds and one double bond to it. For reasons beyond the scope of this Course, the way that the electrons in the double bond are arranged gives rise, in effect, to a kind of 'sea' of electrons above and below the plane of the rings. Three sets of planes are shown in Figure 10.8, although a real sample of graphite would have many planes. The planes are arranged like leaves in a book, or more accurately, like a sheaf of paper. Each plane sits on top of another without being tightly bonded to it. Because the planes are relatively far apart (335 pm) compared with the normal carbon–carbon covalent bond length (142 pm), the attraction between the planes is rather weak.

This leaf structure and the electron sea account for the two main properties of graphite. Its lubricant properties are a result of the readiness with which one layer can slide over another. The other property that we have not mentioned yet is that of electrical conductivity. Conductivity of electricity is a property that is largely confined to metals, with a few exceptions. One of the most important of the exceptions is graphite. If a graphite rod is made part of an electrical circuit then a current will flow. This is most easily (and definitely oversimply) modelled by the idea that if you put electrons in at one end of the sea then others are pushed out at the other end.

The open, layer structure for graphite means it is less dense than diamond. Graphite does not easily melt, but it sublimes at about 3 700 °C, which is close to the temperature needed to melt diamond.

Converts directly to vapour.

10.4 Fullerenes – C_{60} and its family

Until very recently, diamond and graphite were believed to be the only forms of carbon with a regular atomic structure that existed. But in 1985, British and American scientists discovered a completely new form of carbon. Instead of having an extended structure like diamond and graphite, it was believed to consist of just 60 atoms joined together to form the football-shaped structure shown in Figure 10.9. Over the next few years, considerable evidence was gathered to support this structure for C_{60}. However, it took five years of intensive study before it was confirmed unambiguously in 1990 that the structure was indeed that shown in Figure 10.9.

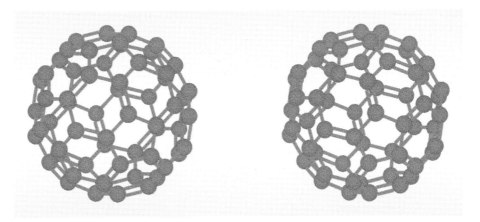

Figure 10.9
Stereoscopic model of buckminsterfullerene, C_{60} – a new form of carbon.

Because of its structure and the similarity with the geodesic dome designed by the architect Buckminster Fuller for the US pavilion at the Montreal Expo of 1967 (Figure 10.10), the new molecule was named buckminsterfullerene. The discovery of this new form of carbon was considered so momentous that buckminsterfullerene was named 'molecule of the year' in 1991 by the journal *Science*.

Figure 10.10
The geodesic dome designed by the architect Buckminster Fuller for the US pavilion at the Montreal Expo of 1967.

Following on rapidly from this discovery came announcements of a second similar molecule with 70 carbon atoms, and subsequently a whole family of related molecules. From the original name for C_{60}, they have been collectively named 'fullerenes'. Such is the interest that this discovery aroused that it stimulated a frenzy of research activity, and over 1 300 research papers were published in the seven years following its initial discovery.

The story of the discovery of buckminsterfullerene and its relatives, now referred to colloquially as 'bucky balls' is admirably and clearly told in an article by Jim Baggott in the 6th July 1991 issue of the popular science journal *New Scientist* (pages 34–38). A reprint of the article is included with your course materials.

Summary of Chapter 10

Carbon is the key element on which life depends. Life itself is based on carbon compounds; we depend on carbon-based fuels for our energy needs; and many modern materials are carbon-based.

Carbon exhibits a rich structural chemistry in its elemental forms. The main ones are diamond, graphite, and a recently discovered family of structures called fullerenes.

Carbon atoms form covalent bonds rather than ions because the latter would mean the formation of either C^{4+} or C^{4-}, which would require a great deal of energy. Instead, carbon achieves the electron configuration of a noble gas by sharing electrons. In methane it does this with four hydrogen atoms; in ethane each carbon atom shares electrons with three hydrogens and another carbon atom. In ethene, carbon shares electrons with only two hydrogen atoms, so it shares two pairs of electrons with a second carbon atom, forming a double covalent bond.

Diamond has a structure based on the same carbon unit found in methane and ethane. It is covalently bonded, so each crystal is a giant molecule. This makes diamond extremely hard. Graphite, which is the stable form of carbon at normal temperatures and pressures, has a structure based on the unit found in ethene and is in the form of layers loosely bonded together. This makes graphite slippery. Graphite also conducts electricity.

In 1985, a new form of carbon was discovered based on the same unit as graphite. Named buckminsterfullerene, it has 60 carbon atoms bonded together in the shape of a sphere, which gave rise to the nickname 'bucky balls'. This discovery has given rise to intense research activity and a whole family of fascinating new fullerenes.

Question 39 Using the same model for sharing electrons as for methane (Figure 10.1), draw out the structure to show how the covalent bonds are formed in water, H_2O.

Question 40 Although chlorine often forms Cl^- ions in its reactions, it can also take part in covalent bonding. An example is the molecule hydrogen chloride, HCl. Using the same model for sharing electrons as for methane (Figure 10.1), draw out the structure to show how the covalent bonds are formed in HCl.

Postscript

In this Book we have travelled a long way. We have examined the beginnings of science from the very dawn of civilization. We have seen how science has developed its various specializations and how the scientific method developed. We have developed a model for matter based on atoms, and have provided much evidence, both indirect and direct, for their existence and properties. And we have seen how this model provides the basis for understanding the chemical properties of matter at the molecular level. You now have at your fingertips a powerful toolkit to use as you study the rest of the Course. In the next three Books, we shall look at a range of molecules that are relevant to such topics as materials, nutrition and health. In so doing, the aim is to show how substances with a whole range of varied properties can be made up from just a few building blocks at the molecular level.

Objectives for Book 1

After you have studied Book 1 you should be able to do the following:

1   Understand the meaning of the words emboldened in the text.

2   Describe in summary form the broad development of science since prehistoric times, and in a sentence or two identify the key differences between the arts and the sciences.

3   (a) Outline the scientific method; (b) identify examples that are consistent or inconsistent with its application; (c) in simple examples, use it correctly, for example to formulate hypotheses.

4   Describe briefly the scope of each of the main scientific disciplines, and recognize the place and scope of chemistry and its relationship with the other disciplines.

5   Understand an article concerned with a scientific and/or technological subject in a newspaper or magazine aimed at the general reader sufficiently to be able to:

    (a) distinguish scientific and technological aspects;
    (b) for scientific aspects, identify the branch of science concerned;
    (c) for technological aspects, identify the scientific basis;
    (d) prepare a summary for someone without a scientific background.

6   (a) Use scientific notation to express large and small numbers; (b) use the SI system of units.

7   Understand and use simple graphs relating two sets of data.

8   Recognize the different states of matter by their distinctive properties.

9   Provide an explanation, in terms of a comparison of the forces involved at the molecular level, for (a) the normal boiling or melting temperature, or the physical state of two or more chemical substances (elements or compounds), or (b) the solubility properties of a liquid or solid in a solvent.

10   (a) Be familiar with and understand the empirical and theoretical basis of the Periodic Table; (b) work out the electron configuration of selected elements and simple compounds in terms of the formation of ions or the sharing of electrons in covalent bonds.

11   (a) Recognize a repeat unit in a geometric array or in a simple crystal lattice; (b) in simple cases, recognize when a molecular structure is the same as a given molecule, an isomer or a molecule of a different substance.

12   (a) Construct physical models of molecules using the model kit provided; (b) use conceptual models of matter to explain observed properties of matter in terms of its structure and behaviour at the molecular level; (c) in simple cases, construct a simple model to explain a given set of observations.

Comments on Activities

Activity 1

At this stage, unless you have done some chemistry before, you will not be able to interpret many of your observations. You may interested to look back, when you reach the end of the Course, to see how your ability to interpret such observations has improved.

The first observation is the ignition of the match on striking it against the side of the matchbox. The flame burns quite fiercely for a few moments and has a different colour from the more gentle yellow flame observed later. The latter is bright yellow at the tip and upper edges but is bluer near the wood of the matchstick. Despite the relatively modest size of the flame, it gives out a surprising amount of heat.

The black residue observed on extinguishing the match is harder to the touch than the wood but crumbles easily. The residue from the substance at the tip of the match does not look materially different from the residue further along the matchstick. Although you could not tell without further experiments, the residue is in fact largely composed of carbon.

In the experiment in which the match was held under the tumbler of cold water, the bottom of the tumbler quickly became cloudy and after a few seconds this turned into tiny droplets of liquid. Although it is not possible to tell without carrying out additional experiments, the droplets are in fact water.

Activity 2

The first of these three news items would probably be regarded by most people as being predominantly a technological development because it depends on known principles for the construction of the drills and the guidance systems necessary to allow successful drilling around a corner and at such a long distance from the drill head. However, it could be argued even here that geological research would have been necessary to increase the chances of success and, as we shall see later, such studies would be regarded as scientific.

The second development is a combination of scientific discovery and technological innovation. The fundamental research into laser physics and the properties of the gallium arsenide would be regarded as producing scientific discoveries; the application of these discoveries to produce a workable device and the incorporation of these devices into a neural network would be technological.

Of the three examples, the third is probably the most purely scientific. The discovery of a new substance and the search for its role in our body chemistry, though its end result might be better treatment of certain disorders, is the result essentially of curiosity, of the desire to find out how our bodies function.

Activity 8

See the answer to Question 11 (p. 177).

Activity 9

A solid is something that has a shape that is independent of its container or its environment and it has a more-or-less fixed volume. To change the shape of a solid some force must be supplied.

A liquid is something that has a fixed volume but takes its shape from its container or its environment. If the shape of a vessel containing a liquid changes then the shape of the liquid will change spontaneously. A moving liquid, like a river, is said to flow.

A gas is something that always completely occupies whatever container it is in. If the volume of its container is increased, then the volume of the gas will increase by exactly the same amount and vice versa.

Activity 11

The main differences are as follows. The ethane molecule has atoms located along all three dimensions and is flexible. The ethene molecule is more rigid and is essentially flat; we say that is has all its atoms lying in the same plane. The ethyne molecule is also rigid, and has its atoms lying in a straight line. These differences between the geometry and rigidity of single, double and triple bonds have profound effects on the properties of compounds with molecules containing these structural features.

Activity 12

Results from weighing gases

Substance	Mass of flask containing fixed volume of gas	Mass of evacuated flask	Mass of gas	Relative molecular mass of substance
hydrogen, H_2	144.174 g	144.162 g	0.012 g	2.0
methane, CH_4	144.275 g	144.162 g	0.113 g	16.0
nitrogen, N_2	144.342 g	144.162 g	0.180 g	28.0
oxygen, O_2	144.363 g	144.162 g	0.201 g	32.0
argon, Ar	144.422 g	144.162 g	0.260 g	39.9
carbon dioxide, CO_2	144.452 g	144.162 g	0.290 g	44.0

Answers to Questions

Question 1 The prime example given in the text is the ability to launch satellites that can be used for a wide range of purposes: for communication, for entertainment, for scientific measurements, for astronomical observations using, for example, the Hubble Space Telescope, for monitoring the Earth's atmosphere and oceans, for mapping the Earth's surface, for prospecting, and for weather forecasting. Other examples that you may have thought of that were not exclusively the result of the space programme, but which it accelerated are: the development of microelectronics; lightweight blankets; advanced materials now used for such things as artificial limbs; materials such as Kevlar, which is as strong as steel but a fraction of the weight; microwave technology that led to microwave ovens; and high-power battery technology. Don't be worried if you weren't aware of any of these; the question was designed simply to start you thinking.

Question 2 There were four main examples cited. You may be aware of the basis for one or more of these from reading newspapers, magazines, and books, or from watching general science programmes on TV. However, don't be worried if you haven't come across any of these; simply use the answer given here as a further source of information.

(a) Chlorofluorocarbons (CFCs) were introduced in the 1930s for use initially as refrigerants. They seemed ideal substances because they are stable and non-toxic. Subsequently, they were used also as blowing agents to make plastic foam, as propellants in spray cans, and as degreasing solvents in the electronics industry. It is their stability in the lower atmosphere, and their susceptibility to being broken down in the stratosphere by the Sun's ultraviolet radiation, that have given rise to the devastating effects on the ozone layer.

(b) The introduction of lead in petrol (as the substance tetraethyllead) was to improve the performance of otherwise lower grade petrol, and thereby reduce losses in refining and hence the eventual cost of petrol.

(c) Acid rain results from the oxides of nitrogen and sulfur that are produced when fuels are burnt, in power stations for example, and in other industrial processes. The need for energy is at the heart of any modern industrialized economy. The nitrogen oxides are formed because of the high temperatures, which cause nitrogen from the atmosphere to combine with oxygen. The sulfur oxides come from sulfur, which is an impurity in oil and coal.

(d) Plants such as crops grown for food need supplies of nitrogen in a readily accessible form. Only very few plants are able to make use of nitrogen from the air directly. Nitrogen in the form of nitrate is a convenient and easily applied method of supplying nitrogen to crops. Nitrates dissolve readily in water, which makes them easy to apply by spraying; it also means, unfortunately, that they are readily washed off by rain and the run-off accumulates in ponds, lakes and underground aquifers.

Note that environmentally friendly alternatives have been, or are in the process of being, developed for most of these applications.

Question 3   The following typical description of burning wood in terms of the four Aristotelian elements is taken from Marie Boas, 'An early version of the *Sceptical Chymist*', *Isis*, 1954, vol. 45, pp. 153–68:

> *The experiment commonly alledged for the common opinion of the four elements, is, that if a green stick be burned in the naked fire, there will first fly away a smoake, which argued AIRE, then will boyle out at the ends a certain liquor, which is supposed WATER, the FIRE dissolves itself by its own light, and that incombustible part it leaves at last, is nothing but the element of EARTH.*

In terms of the match, the fire is obviously present; the smoke is supposed to be carried by air; the liquid that condenses on the glass is water; and the ash remaining is taken to be earth.

Question 4   (a) The development of an irrigation system would be classified as technology because it would have depended on the application of known principles to a practical problem.

(b) As you will see in Section 3.4, the attempted conversion of base metals into gold (a process we now know is not possible by chemical means) was one of the prime activities of alchemy. Though it had certain aspects that we might regard as being scientific given the state of knowledge at the time, much of the driving force was philosophical because gold was regarded as the state of perfection for material bodies.

(c) This is a fine example of the empirical method and is undoubtedly scientific.

(d) This is partly philosophical because placing the Earth at the centre of the Universe and the movement of the other planets in circles were based on philosophical beliefs, and it is partly scientific because it was an attempt to form a hypothesis based on astronomical observations.

(e) This involves both craft and technology in the production of the bronze vessel and its decoration. It would also have involved technology, and possibly science, in the methods used to obtain the bronze by extracting the constituent tin and copper from ores containing these metals.

(f) This is pure science. It involves observation and recording of events for future use, together with classification based on intrinsic properties rather than any philosophical framework imposed by Hipparchus.

Question 5   (a) The development of new dyes would involve scientific and technological inputs to decide on the substances that would have the desired colour(s) and to develop efficient methods of manufacture. However, considerations relating to the aesthetics of the colours produced would be neither scientific nor technological.

(b) The book in question would undoubtedly be a work of art and could be enjoyed as such. However, it would also be a most useful aid to botanical studies of lilies, and indeed was primarily intended for this purpose, and consequently is scientific in nature.

(c) The JET project is primarily scientific/technological in its aims. However, the decision to site it in the UK rather than some other European country was largely political.

(d) The THORP project is a highly controversial one, with the inevitable risks involved in handling highly radioactive material. The expertise involved in the design and construction would have been largely scientific and technological. However, other, largely political and economic, considerations entered into the decision to construct it and will influence its future role in the nuclear industry.

(e) The process of restoring old paintings involves a great deal of scientific expertise to choose the best cleansing agents and procedures. However, the controversial decision to carry out the restoration in the first place and the question as to whether the restored painting is more or less true to Michelangelo's intentions are non-scientific issues.

Question 6 Your hypothesis concerning the effect of the length of the pendulum on the period of swing could be: (i) the longer the pendulum the longer the period; (ii) the longer the pendulum the shorter the period; or (iii) the length of the pendulum has no effect on the period.

Whichever you chose, the hypothesis would be tested by measuring the period of swing of pendulums of different lengths. In doing this it would be necessary to choose an appropriate range of lengths: for example, a series of pendulums of lengths 100 cm, 102 cm, 104 cm, 106 cm, 108 cm and 110 cm is likely to be too small a range; a series of pendulums of lengths 1 m, 5 m, 10 m and 20 m is likely to be impracticably large. It would also be necessary to arrange a method of determining when the pendulum passed the checkpoint and to time the period with sufficient accuracy. For example, a clock with a minute hand would be too inaccurate; a stopwatch reading to tenths of a second would be satisfactory; an electronic timing device triggered by the pendulum breaking an infrared beam would be even better.

Your hypothesis concerning the effect of mass on the period of swing could be: (i) that the heavier the bob the longer the period; (ii) the heavier the bob the shorter the period; or (iii) the mass of the bob has no effect on the period. Whichever you chose, similar considerations hold for testing the hypothesis as for the effect of length, except that this time you would need to time the periods of pendulums with bobs of different masses.

Note that for the dependence of period on pendulum length, you should use the same bob for each pendulum. For the dependence of period on bob mass, you should keep the length of the pendulum the same. In scientific language, we say that you should change only one variable at a time. If not, you would not be able to decide what any variations in the periods that you found were due to.

You may like to know that the longer the pendulum, the longer the period of swing. However, the period of swing does *not* depend on the mass of the pendulum bob, a result which may well go against your intuition. This is a good example of the need to make careful measurements and observations *before* coming to a conclusion about the correctness or otherwise of a given hypothesis.

Question 7 (a) The purpose of launching the UARS is clearly primarily scientific, so that observations of the chemistry of the upper atmosphere can be made. Equally clearly, without the space technology required to make the satellite and to launch it, the observations would not be possible. This is a prime example of the application of advanced technology for scientific purposes.

(b) It could be argued that this is primarily a technological advance since the properties of titanium that make it suitable had already been discovered. However, it could also be argued that the initial trials, at least, were scientific in that medical studies would have been needed to make sure that the necessary bonding had taken place and that no unwanted side-effects occurred.

(c) This announcement was possible as a result of scientific studies by chemists to enable new sweeteners to be designed and made. Regardless of whether you believe that artificial sweeteners are a good thing or not, the discovery of what appears to be an improved sugar substitute required extensive scientific research. Technology would have been involved in the sense that various instruments would have been used in the research, and manufacture on a large scale would also have been substantially a technological problem.

(d) This is primarily a technological example. The properties of barium hydroxide that make it suitable as a medium for storing heat have been known for some time. Working out the most effective design for the device would have involved primarily technological skills.

Question 8 (a) Because energy and novel materials are both involved with this topic, it could involve materials scientists, physicists or chemists. It does not impinge on biology or Earth sciences.

(b) This clearly has aspects that relate to chemistry and to biology, mainly biochemistry and molecular biology.

(c) Earth sciences is undoubtedly relevant in this case. However, the conversion of coal into useful fuels is of concern to chemists, and the energetics involved impinge on physics.

(d) The depletion of ozone is primarily an effect of chemical reactions caused by the decomposition of chlorofluorocarbons (CFCs) by sunlight and so is directly of interest to chemists. However, because the extent and timing of the ozone depletion is also a function of the detailed motion of the stratosphere, it is also the concern of Earth scientists, primarily atmospheric scientists.

(e) This is almost completely the concern of biologists, particularly biochemists, geneticists and molecular biologists. However, some of the techniques and methodology used are also used by chemists working in the biomedical area.

Question 9 Because all matter was thought to be composed of the four elements in different proportions, it should be possible in principle to alter the existing proportions of the various elements to the proportions present in gold. Because gold is a metal, it also made sense to use other metals as a starting point because they shared many of the attributes of gold already.

Question 10 (a) The curve showing the number of documents per year reached the 100 000 mark in about 1956.

(b) The number abstracted in 1975 was about ~~330 000.~~ 400,000

(c) The number abstracted per year fell, not surprisingly, during the war years in 1914–1918 and 1939–1945. Perhaps more surprisingly, it has also fallen more recently in the period around 1979–1980.

If you have had no previous experience of reading data from graphs, you should refer to AV sequence 1.

Question 11 Here are some possible questions that arise from the article. What are polychlorinated biphenyls (PCBs)? Why are they toxic? Why is burning them an unacceptable solution? What transformations are involved in converting PCBs and other toxic substances into carbon dioxide and water? What is the nature of the residue? What does an electrochemical cell look like? What is the silver salt that was used? What is the role of the nitric acid? What is nitric acid? How can it cope with such a wide range of materials?

You may have thought of different questions, but the list here will give you enough examples to enable you to check any of your own suggestions that are different.

Question 12 For the largest-scale map, 1 mm represents 10 000 mm, or 10 m, or 0.01 km. You have to divide the number of millimetres by 1 000 to get the number of metres, and by another 1 000 to get the number of kilometres. For this map, the scale most easy to appreciate is 1 mm equals 10 m.

You may be interested to know the scales of the other maps. For (b), 1 mm represents 200 000 mm, or 200 m, or 0.2 km; for (c), 1 mm represents 100 000 mm, or 100 m, or 0.1 km; for (d), 1 mm represents 50 000 mm, or 50 m, or 0.05 km; and for (e), 1 mm represents 20 000 mm, or 20 m, or 0.02 km.

Question 13 Representing the three numbers in scientific notation, 10 is 10^1, 1 000 is 10^3 and 100 is 10^2. So to multiply the three numbers together, you need to add the powers giving $1 + 3 + 2 = 6$. So the answer is 10^6 or 1 000 000. You can easily verify the answer by working it out longhand or by using your calculator.

Question 14 Using scientific notation the multiplication $3\,625 \times 284$ can be written as follows: $(3.625 \times 10^3) \times (2.84 \times 10^2)$. To obtain the answer, since a series of multiplications can be carried out in any order, this can be written as $3.625 \times 2.84 \times 10^3 \times 10^2$, which (remembering to add the exponents) equals 10.295×10^5 or (remembering that the number multiplying the power of ten is usually chosen to lie between 1 and 9.999…) $1.029\,5 \times 10^6$.

Question 15 Since the plan is drawn to a scale of $1 : 20$, 1 mm on the plan represents 20 mm (2 cm or 0.02 m) in reality. Conversely, a distance of 1 m (100 cm) is represented on the plan as 5 cm. So a kitchen measuring 3.6 m by 4.2 m would appear on the plan as a rectangle (360/20) cm by (420/20) cm, that is 18 cm by 21 cm.

Question 16 Using scientific notation, the multiplication 0.25×0.04 can be written as follows: $(2.5 \times 10^{-1}) \times (4.0 \times 10^{-2})$. To obtain the answer, remembering that a series of multiplications can be carried out in any order, this can be written as $2.5 \times 4.0 \times 10^{-1} \times 10^{-2}$, which (remembering to add the exponents) equals 10.0×10^{-3} or (remembering that the number multiplying the power of ten is usually chosen to lie between 1 and 9.99…) 1.0×10^{-2}. This can also simply be written as 10^{-2}.

Question 17 On Earth the gold bar would give a reading of about 960 g. Because the balance would have been calibrated against a standard mass, this tells us the mass of the bar. However, the reading is the result of the gravitational attraction on the gold bar. Taking the gold bar to the Moon would not change its mass, because that is an intrinsic property of the bar. However, the weighing process depends on the gravitational attraction by the Moon on the gold bar, which would be only one-sixth as strong. Consequently, the (misleading) reading would be only 160 g (that is, 960 g divided by 6).

Question 18 The force exerted by your thumb is spread over the relatively wide area of the head of the drawing pin and so the pressure is much less than at the point where the same force is concentrated on a very small area. The resulting high pressure allows the point to penetrate the wood.

Question 19 Like most foodstuffs, even if nominally dried, popcorn kernels contain some water. Placing them in hot oil or a microwave oven causes the water to vaporize. Because of the huge increase in volume on vaporization, the popcorn kernel becomes 'puffed up' as the steam attempts to escape.

Question 20 Heating the air enclosed in the balloon canopy causes it to expand. As the neck of the canopy is open, some of the air escapes into the surrounding atmosphere. Because of the expansion, the air in the canopy is less dense than the surrounding air. Just as ice cubes float in liquid water because they are less dense, the balloon experiences an upward force, which allows it to float in the air.

Question 21 (a) 8×10^{-8} m; (b) $8 \times 10^{-2}\,\mu$m ; (c) 80 nm. This corresponds to a thickness of about 270 atoms.

Perhaps the simplest way to tackle this question is first to convert the thickness in millimetres into scientific notation. So 0.000 08 mm is then 8×10^{-5} mm, since the decimal place is moved five places to the right. Then remembering that 1 mm = 10^{-3} m, this becomes 8×10^{-8} m (that is $8 \times 10^{-5} \times 10^{-3}$ m). Similarly, 8×10^{-5} mm expressed in micrometres (remembering that 1 micrometre = $1\,\mu$m = 10^{-6} m = 10^{-3} mm) becomes $8 \times 10^{-2}\,\mu$m. And expressed in nanometres, remembering that 1 nm = 10^{-9} m = 10^{-6} mm, 8×10^{-5} mm becomes 80 nm.

The diameter of a gold atom is 3×10^{-10} m, so a thickness of 8×10^{-8} m corresponds to $(8 \times 10^{-8}$ m$) \div (3 \times 10^{-10}$ m$)$ atoms, which is about 270.

Question 22 (a) A hydrogen atom has a nucleus consisting of a single proton with a single electron in the space surrounding it; a proton is just that, with no electron associated.

(b) A proton is the positively charged elementary particle found in the nuclei of all elements; a neutron has approximately the same mass as a proton, but is neutral (that is, it has no electrical charge) and is found in the nuclei of all elements except hydrogen (it is found in the isotope of hydrogen called deuterium).

Question 23 Because the atomic number of magnesium is 12, this tells us the number of protons in the nucleus is 12. This also means that there are 12 electrons. As the relative atomic mass of this magnesium isotope is 24.0, the remaining mass of 12 units must be made up of neutrons; hence there are 12 neutrons.

Question 24 The chemical formula of the compound hydrogen sulfide is written H_2S.

Question 25 One repeat unit is shown in Figure A1a. The sequence in each direction, both vertically and horizontally, is red, green, red, blue, and then it starts to repeat. One repeat unit therefore is as shown. Other, similar ones are possible based on moving along and/or up by one dot each time. Each one must be the same size as Figure A1a; another possibility is shown as Figure A1b.

Figure A1
(a) One possible repeat unit; (b) another possible repeat unit.

Question 26 Model A is a different isomer of the molecules in Figure 7.42: it has a longest chain of four carbon atoms, not five. Model B is the same as Figure 7.42a, but turned and twisted a little. Similarly, model C is the same as Figure 7.42b. Model D has a different chemical formula, because it has seven carbon atoms, not six. Model E is the same as model B, but turned sideways. Model F is the same as model C, but turned upside down.

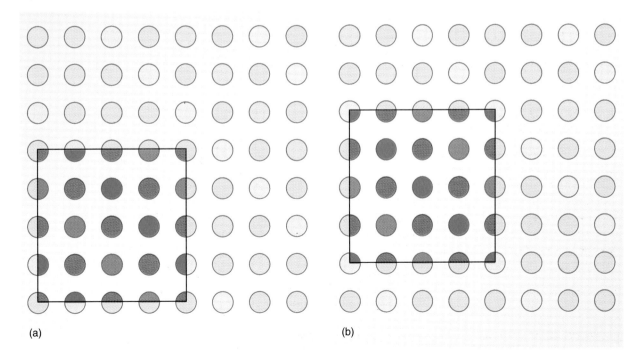

(a)   (b)

Question 27 The London forces are greater between CBr_4 molecules than they are between CCl_4 molecules. This is because bromine atoms have more electrons than chlorine atoms and hence are more polarizable. Since neither molecule has an overall dipole, different dipole–dipole forces cannot be the reason. And since neither molecule has a hydrogen atom connected to an oxygen or nitrogen atom, hydrogen bonding can't be involved either.

Question 28 Pure water freezes at $0\,°C$. However, dissolving anything in water lowers the freezing temperature. It seems reasonable to predict that as more solute is added, the more the freezing temperature will be lowered. Because a considerable amount of ethane-1,2-diol is added to produce the mixture that is used, the freezing temperature is likely to be lowered considerably. In fact, it is lowered to about $-11\,°C$, coincidentally the same as the freezing temperature of pure ethane-1,2-diol.

Question 29 Although ionic compounds would be expected to show the same effect, they melt at very high temperatures. This means that it is much more difficult to measure the melting temperature than for molecular solids.

Question 30 You would see a shiny molten metal at the cathode and a brown fuming liquid at the anode. By analogy with the electrolysis of molten sodium chloride, lithium cations would migrate towards the cathode, where they would gain an electron and be converted into lithium atoms. The lithium atoms would then combine together to form lithium metal. Similarly, the bromide anions would migrate towards the anode, where they would lose an electron and be converted into bromine atoms. These atoms would combine to form bromine molecules, and hence bromine liquid.

Question 31 Like most foodstuffs, even if nominally dried, popcorn kernels contain some water. Placing them in hot oil or a microwave oven heats up the water. The energy transferred on heating causes progressively more vigorous motion of the water molecules. Eventually, this motion becomes so vigorous that it overcomes even the relatively strong hydrogen bonds holding the water molecules together, and the water boils. Because of the huge increase in volume, the popcorn kernel becomes 'puffed up' as the steam attempts to escape.

Question 32 One mole of helium (or any gas) occupies 24.5 litres at $25\,°C$. So 2.45 litres should be $2.45/24.5$ mol, which equals 0.1 mol. Since one mole of any gas occupies 24.5 litres at that temperature, 0.1 mol would occupy 2.45 litres. Hence a flask of the same size containing hydrogen gas would also contain 0.1 mol.

Question 33 Because potassium has 19 protons in the nucleus it will have 19 electrons. The first two electrons will go into the 1s sub-shell; two will go into the 2s sub-shell and six into the 2p sub-shell; then two more electrons will go into the 3s sub-shell and six into the 3p sub-shell. This leaves one electron to go into the 4s sub-shell. The electron configuration is therefore $1s^2 2s^2 2p^6 3s^2 3p^6 4s^1$, or $[Ar]4s^1$. So, just as with lithium and sodium, potassium in its reactions will readily lose an electron to form a positive ion, K^+, which has the same electron configuration as the noble gas argon.

Question 34 [He]$2s^2 2p^3$. The atomic number of nitrogen is 7 so it has seven electrons. These will go into the sub-shells as follows: two into the 1s, two into the 2s and three into the 2p. A quicker way is to note that helium has an atomic number of 2 so it has two electrons. This leaves five to go into the sub-shells that fill after helium (2s and 2p). This method is particularly useful for elements with higher atomic numbers.

Question 35 [Ne]$3s^2$. The atomic number of magnesium is 12 so it has 12 electrons. The atomic number of neon is 10 so it has 10 electrons. This leaves just two to go into the sub-shell that follows neon (3s), giving the answer.

Question 36 [Ar]$3d^{10}4s^2 4p^5$. The atomic number of bromine is 35 so it has 35 electrons. The atomic number of argon is 18 so it has 18 electrons. This leaves 17 to go into the sub-shells that follow argon (4s, 3d, 4p), giving the answer. Note that the 3d sub-shell fills *after* the 4s, but in writing the electron configuration it is put *in front of* the 4s sub-shell.

Question 37 Aluminium has an atomic number of 13 and so has 13 electrons. It has three more electrons than neon (atomic number 10) and so it is likely to form Al^{3+} ions in its reactions. (The 3+ means three positive charges.)

Question 38 The halogens are the elements in the Group next to the noble gases and are headed by fluorine (F). The other members are chlorine (Cl), bromine (Br), iodine (I), and astatine (At). (You may be interested to know that astatine is a radioactive element and so usually the halogens are taken to be only the other four elements.)

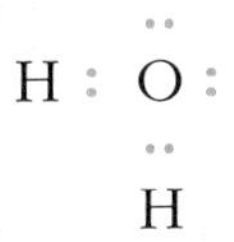

Question 39 The arrangement of electrons in the water molecule is shown in Figure A2. Oxygen has an atomic number of 8 and so has eight electrons. It therefore has two electrons fewer than the nearest noble gas, neon, which has 10. Just as with carbon, it can obtain the two electrons necessary to achieve the noble gas configuration by sharing, in this case with hydrogen. In so doing, the hydrogen atoms attain the helium configuration. The two pairs of electrons not involved in bonding are called, imaginatively(!), 'non-bonded pairs'.

Question 40 The arrangement of electrons in the hydrogen chloride molecule is shown in Figure A3. Chlorine has an atomic number of 17 and so has 17 electrons. It therefore has one electron fewer than the nearest noble gas, argon, which has 18. Just as with carbon, it can obtain the one electron necessary to achieve the noble gas configuration by sharing, in this case with hydrogen. In so doing, the hydrogen atom also attains the helium configuration.

H : O :

H

Figure A2
The electron configuration of water.

H : Cl :

Figure A3
The electron configuration of hydrogen chloride.

Appendix: the elements

At present 109 elements are known: 94 occur naturally on Earth and the rest have been made by nuclear processes in which atoms of certain elements are bombarded by particles such as neutrons, alpha-particles (essentially helium nuclei containing two protons and two neutrons), or positive ions of the lighter elements such as boron, carbon, nitrogen or oxygen. In many instances, the initially formed nucleus is unstable and subsequently undergoes radioactive decay to give a different, more stable isotope. Elements 104–109 have been made only a few atoms at a time, and few of their properties are known. In the light of rival claims for priority of discovery, scientists have still not agreed formally what these elements should be called. Accordingly, we have left these six elements out of the following table.

Studies of the composition of the Earth's crust have shown that the element oxygen accounts for about 46% by weight of the crust, silicon about 27%, and aluminium about 8%. These three elements, together with iron, calcium, sodium, potassium and magnesium, account for about 99% of the crust's composition. Of the elements thought to be essential for life, the four most abundant by far are carbon, hydrogen, nitrogen and oxygen; the next most abundant are calcium, phosphorus, chlorine, potassium, sulfur, sodium, and magnesium. The elements iron, copper, zinc, silicon, iodine, cobalt, manganese, molybdenum, fluorine, tin, chromium, selenium and vanadium are also needed in trace amounts.

Element	Symbol	Atomic number	Relative atomic mass	Date of discovery	Melting temperature in °C	Boiling temperature in °C
actinium*	Ac	89	227	1899	1 047	3 197
aluminium	Al	13	27.0	1825	660	2 467
americium*	Am	95	243	1944	994	2 607
antimony	Sb	51	122	before 1600	631	1 635
argon	Ar	18	39.9	1894	−189	−186
arsenic	As	33	74.9	1250	616 (sublimes)	—
astatine*	At	85	210	1940	302	337
barium	Ba	56	137	1808	729	1 637
berkelium*	Bk	97	247	1949	n.a.	n.a.
beryllium	Be	4	9.01	1797	1 278	2 970
bismuth	Bi	83	209	1753	271	1 560
boron	B	5	10.8	1808	2 300	3 658
bromine	Br	35	79.9	1826	−7	59
cadmium	Cd	48	112	1817	321	765
caesium	Cs	55	133	1860	28	678
calcium	Ca	20	40.1	1808	839	1 484
californium*	Cf	98	251	1950	n.a.	n.a.
carbon	C	6	12.0	prehistoric	3 550 (diamond)	4 830
cerium	Ce	58	140	1803	799	3 426
chlorine	Cl	17	35.5	1774	−101	−34
chromium	Cr	24	52.0	1780	1 857	2 672
cobalt	Co	27	58.9	1735	1 495	2 870
copper	Cu	29	63.5	ancient	1 083	2 567
curium*	Cm	96	247	1944	1 337	n.a.
dysprosium	Dy	66	163	1886	1 412	2 562
einsteinium*	Es	99	254	1952	n.a.	n.a.
erbium	Er	68	167	1842	1 529	2 863
europium	Eu	63	152	1901	822	1 597
fermium*	Fm	100	257	1952	n.a.	n.a.
fluorine	F	9	19.0	1886	−220	−188
francium*	Fr	87	223	1939	27	677
gadolinium	Gd	64	157	1880	1 313	3 266
gallium	Ga	31	69.7	1875	30	2 403
germanium	Ge	32	72.6	1886	937	2 830
gold	Au	79	197	ancient	1 064	2 807
hafnium	Hf	72	178	1923	2 230	5 197
helium	He	2	4.00	1895	−272	−269

Element	Symbol	Atomic number	Relative atomic mass	Date of discovery	Melting temperature in °C	Boiling temperature in °C
holmium	Ho	67	165	1878	1474	2695
hydrogen	H	1	1.01	1766	−259	−253
indium	In	49	115	1863	156	2080
iodine	I	53	127	1811	114	184
iridium	Ir	77	192	1803	2410	4130
iron	Fe	26	55.8	ancient	1535	2750
krypton	Kr	36	83.8	1898	−157	−152
lanthanum	La	57	139	1839	921	3457
lawrencium*	Lr	103	262	1961	n.a.	n.a.
lead	Pb	82	207	ancient	328	1740
lithium	Li	3	6.94	1817	181	1347
lutetium	Lu	71	175	1907	1663	3395
magnesium	Mg	12	24.3	1755	649	1090
manganese	Mn	25	54.9	1774	1244	1962
mendelevium*	Md	101	258	1955	n.a.	n.a.
mercury	Hg	80	201	ancient	−39	357
molybdenum	Mo	42	95.9	1781	2617	4612
neodymium	Nd	60	144	1885	1021	3068
neon	Ne	10	20.2	1898	−249	−246
neptunium*	Np	93	237	1940	640	3902
nickel	Ni	28	58.7	1751	1453	2732
niobium	Nb	41	92.9	1801	2468	4742
nitrogen	N	7	14.0	1772	−210	−196
nobelium*	No	102	259	1958	n.a.	n.a.
osmium	Os	76	190	1803	3054	5027
oxygen	O	8	16.0	1774	−218	−183
palladium	Pd	46	106	1803	1552	3140
phosphorus	P	15	31.0	1669	44	280
platinum	Pt	78	195	1750	1772	3827
plutonium*	Pu	94	244	1940	641	3232
polonium*	Po	84	209	1898	254	962
potassium	K	19	39.1	1807	64	774
praseodymium	Pr	59	141	1885	931	3512
promethium*	Pm	61	145	1945	1168	ca. 2700
protactinium*	Pa	91	231	1917	1840	4027
radium*	Ra	88	226	1898	700	1140
radon*	Rn	86	222	1900	−71	−62
rhenium	Re	75	186	1925	3180	5627
rhodium	Rh	45	103	1803	1966	3727
rubidium	Rb	37	85.5	1861	39	688

Element	Symbol	Atomic number	Relative atomic mass	Date of discovery	Melting temperature in °C	Boiling temperature in °C
ruthenium	Ru	44	101	1808	2 310	3 900
samarium	Sm	62	150	1879	1 077	1 791
scandium	Sc	21	45.0	1879	1 541	2 831
selenium	Se	34	79.0	1817	217	685
silicon	Si	14	28.1	1824	1 410	2 355
silver	Ag	47	108	ancient	962	2 212
sodium	Na	11	23.0	1807	98	883
strontium	Sr	38	87.6	1790	769	1 384
sulfur	S	16	32.1	ancient	113	445
tantalum	Ta	73	181	1802	2 996	5 425
technetium*	Tc	43	98.9	1937	2 172	4 877
tellurium	Te	52	128	1783	450	990
terbium	Tb	65	159	1843	1 356	3 123
thallium	Tl	81	204	1861	304	1 457
thorium*	Th	90	232	1815	1 750	4 787
thulium	Tm	69	169	1879	1 545	1 947
tin	Sn	50	119	ancient	232	2 270
titanium	Ti	22	47.9	1791	1 660	3 287
tungsten	W	74	184	1783	3 407	5 657
uranium*	U	92	238	1789	1 132	3 745
vanadium	V	23	50.9	1801	1 887	3 377
xenon	Xe	54	131	1898	−112	−107
ytterbium	Yb	70	173	1878	824	1 193
yttrium	Y	39	88.9	1794	1 522	3 338
zinc	Zn	30	65.4	before 1500	420	907
zirconium	Zr	40	91.2	1789	1 852	4 377

n.a. not available

*Has no stable isotope, that is all the isotopes are radioactive. In the majority of such cases, the relative atomic mass refers to the longest-lived isotope.

Index

Acknowledgements

Grateful acknowledgement is made to the following sources for permission
to reproduce material in this book:

Text

Box 2.2 Reprinted by permission of the publishers and the Loeb Classical
Library from Frank Grainger, Vitruvius On Architecture, Vol II, Cambridge,
Mass.: Harvard University Press, 1934; Nicholson-Lord, D. (1993) 'Failure to
act on toxic apple juice attacked', *The Independent*, 11 February 1993;
Mowbray, P. (1992) 'Cancer: a new way out', *Sunday Times Magazine*, 26
July 1992, © Times Newspapers Ltd 1992; Wolmar, C. (1992) 'Buses to use
rape seed fuel for trial period', *The Independent*, 3 November 1992;
Matthews, R. (1987) 'Taking the heat out of man-made fibres', *The Times*, 1
May, 1987, © Times Newspapers Ltd 1987; Bradshaw, D. (1993) 'On the scent
of a bestsmeller', *The Financial Times*, 12 February 1993; Bird, J. (1989)
'"Silver bullet" kills toxic waste', *Sunday Times*, 24 September 1989, © Times
Newspapers Ltd 1989; *Box 5.1* Anderton, P. 'Which units of length?'.

Figures

Figures 1.1, 2.1 NASA; *Figures 1.2, 1.3* Gallagher B. (1989), Never Beyond
Reach, Copyright © International Maritime Satellite Organization 1989;
Figures 1.4, 1.5 Allstock, Seattle; *Figures 1.6, 5.1* Sidney Harris; *Figure 1.7*
British Gas; *Figure 2.2* Jean Vertut; *Figure 2.3* Courtesy of Private Eye; *Figure
2.5*: Luton Museum & Art Gallery; *Figure 2.6* Ancient Art and Architecture
Collection; *Figures 2.7, 2.13, 9.2* Ancient Art and Architecture Collection;
Figure 2.8 Robert Estall Photographs; *Figure 2.9* Dr R.J.C. Atkinson,
University College, Cardiff; *Figure 2.10* Dr J.M. Whitehead; *Figures 2.11,
2.25, 3.6, 6.16, 8.10, 8.20* Science Photo Library; *Figure 2.12* Geoscience
Features Picture Library; *Figure 2.14* National Portrait Gallery, London;
Figures 2.15, 3.2 Mansell Collection; *Figures 2.16, 3.3, 7.2, 7.7, 8.17, 9.3*
Reproduced courtesy of the Library and Information Centre of the Royal
Society of Chemistry; *Figure 2.19* Sydney Hoff/The New Yorker, 28th
September, 1957; *Figure 2.20* Reprinted with kind permission of 3M
Healthcare Ltd; *Figure 2.21a, b* Photographic Service, CERN, Geneva; *Figures
2.22, 3.10, 7.3, 7.32, 8.24* Science Museum; *Figure 2.23* European Space
Agency; *Figure 2.24* Courtesy of Coherent (UK) Ltd; *Figures 3.1, 6.10, 8.16,
10.10* Dr D.R. Roberts; *Figure 3.4* Rijksmuseum, Amsterdam; *Figure 3.5*
Antony Barrington Brown; *Figures 3.7, 8.18* Hulton-Deutsch Picture
Collection; *Figure 3.8* National Gallery of Scotland; *Figure 3.9* Florence
Palazzo Vecchio Photo: Scala; *Figures 3.11, 8.23* Sheridan Muspratt's
Chemistry, Theoretical, Practical and Analytical (1853); *Figure 3.14* Schulz,
H., From CA To CAS Online, VCH Verlagsgesellschaft mbH; *Figure 3.15*
Chemical Abstracts Service and Chemistry International, 1993, Vol. 15, No 3;
Figures 5.2, 5.5 Bureau International des Poids et Mesures; *Figure 5.6a, b* AA
Great Britain Road Atlas 1994, © The Automobile Association June 1994;
Figure 5.6c Bartholemew Cambridge & Bedford Leisure Map, ©
Bartholemew, 1990, A Division of HarperCollins Publishers. Reproduced with

permission; *Figure 5.6d* Reproduced from Ordnance Survey mapping with the permission of the Controller of Her Majesty's Stationery Office. © Crown Copyright; *Figures 5.6e, f* Excerpts from The 1994 Official City Map of Milton Keynes, Geo Projects, © Commission for the New Towns; *Figures 5.7, 5.8, 5.9, 5.10, 5.11, 5.12, 5.13, 5.14, 5.15, 5.16, 5.17, 5.18, 5.19. 5.20* from Powers of Ten, by Eames and Morrison. Copyright © 1982 by Scientific American Library. Reprinted with permission of W.H.Freeman and Company; *Figure 6.5* Courtesy of Sartorius Ltd; *Figures 6.6, 7.1* Tony Stone Images/ Patrick Ingrand; *Figure 6.7* Heather Clarke; *Figure 6.9* Ursula Snowden; *Figure 6.14* Spencer Swanger/Tom Stack & Associates; *Figure 7.6a* courtesy of Topometrix Corporation; *Figure 7.9* Dr S.W. Bennett; *Figure 7.27* National Cycle Museum; *Figure 8.14a* Dowty Aerospace Landing Gear Ltd; *Figure 8.15* Professor B.J. Alder, University of California; *Figure 9.1 The Independent*; *Figures 10.4, 10.5, 10.6* de Beers/Centenary.

Offprints attached to Book 1

Jones, D. (1994), 'Daedalus', *The Guardian*, 15 January 1994; Extract from 'Ariadne', *New Scientist*, 3 November 1966, IPC Magazines Ltd; Baggott, J. (1991) 'Great balls of carbon', New Scientist, Vol. 131, No 1776, 6 July 1991, IPC Magazines Ltd. Photos/Illustrations: p. 35: Osnat Lippa; p. 36: Clive Freeman, The Royal Institution/SPL; p. 38 (top left): Rice University; p. 38 (top right): University of Sussex; p. 38 (centre): Max Planck Institute for Nuclear Physics; p. 38 (bottom): Robert Wilson/IBM Almaden.